Burma Campaign
Memorial Library

IN MEMORY OF ALL
WHO PARTICIPATED AND THE
MANY WHO DIED

BURMA 1942–45

Blossoms fall to earth
The pagoda promises
That spring will follow

Burma Campaign Memorial Library

A collection of books
and papers about the
War in Burma 1942–1945

Compiled by
Gordon Graham MC MA D UNIV STIRLING and
Frank Cole FLA

School of Oriental and African Studies
London 1999

© School of Oriental and African Studies
Thornhaugh Street
Russell Square
London WC1H 0XG

First published 1999

ISBN 0 7286 0305 5

THIS CATALOGUE MAY BE
PURCHASED FROM THE SOAS
BOOKSHOP.

£10

£5 for veterens

Typesetting Margaret Mills
Design and Production Douglas Williamson
Printed by Redwood Books Ltd, Trowbridge

Introduction

THE IDEA of a Memorial Library on the Burma Campaign first arose in 1995, when it was observed that there was no single comprehensive collection of books on what had been the longest continuous campaign of World War II. Would not such a collection be a fitting memorial to the tragedy and heroism and futility of war; a treasure house for the dwindling brotherhood who had participated in the campaign; a resource for future scholars and historians; and a measure of insurance that a campaign overshadowed at the time by the vast events in Europe and the Pacific, should not become a mere footnote to history?

As a first step, lists were obtained from the British National Bibliography, Whitaker's Cumulative Database, the Bodleian Library and the Imperial War Museum. The Burma section of A. G. Enser's 1975 Subject Bibliography of Second World War Books in English was consulted, as were specialized bibliographies such as 'English-Language Fiction about the War in Burma' compiled by Lewis Hill of the University of Hull. Lists of books in personal libraries were volunteered. Authors' bibliographies at the ends of their books were scanned. Privately published books and unpublished manuscripts came to light.

So began what proved to be a four-year project, consisting initially of pledges of books from personal libraries. Parting with treasured books is hard, so those who did not feel ready to donate their books in their lifetimes were invited to leave instructions to their heirs. Such personal gifts and bequests are the largest component of the Memorial Library. On the flyleaf of each donated book is a bookplate giving the name and details of service of the donor, who in some cases is also the author.

Soon the search, aided by networking among members of the Burma Star Association and many reunion groups, became international. The war in Burma had involved the forces of many nations. In addition to books published in Britain, which constitute the majority of the collection, there are books from the United States, India, Burma, Australia and Canada. There are also a few books translated from Japanese into English, and a start has been made, with the help of the All-Burma Veterans' Association of Japan, in assembling a collection of Japanese books.

After two years of voluntary effort, it became clear that finance was needed to complete the project. The Burma Campaign Fellowship Group, which, since it was founded in 1990, has done much to improve understanding between Japanese and British veterans, made an application to the Great Britain Sasakawa Foundation for funds, not only to buy books, but to contribute to the installation and upkeep of the Library.

To back this application, it was necessary first to find a permanent home for the Library, where it would be easily accessible to present and future generations. An approach was made to the Library of the School of Oriental and African Studies (SOAS), which is the premier centre for Asian studies in the UK and has an historical connection with the war in Japan, since it provided crash courses in the Japanese language during World War II. The SOAS Library not only agreed to house the Memorial Library as a discrete collection, but to integrate with it relevant titles already in their collections.

After securing this generous help from the GB Sasakawa Foundation and SOAS, a further two years were spent in tracking down and purchasing rare titles, mainly through booksellers specialising in military history. There was also substantial correspondence with veterans of the Burma war in many parts of the world. Valuable manuscripts which were in danger of oblivion were uncovered. By early 1999, about 600 of the 750 titles in the bibliography had been acquired, a sufficient number to justify the transfer of the collection to SOAS and its public inauguration.

The launch of the Library is not the end of the project. Titles still to be acquired will be added. Unrecorded titles will be identified. New books are being written, and there will be more books in the future. A library is a living thing. In the care of skilled librarians it will last for hundreds of years. Its purpose is not merely to store knowledge and impart information, but to stimulate thought. Libraries are the vehicles which pass, from generation to generation, the lessons learned, wisdom, experience, and, less deliberately, insight into the follies of those who have gone before. In the Burma Campaign Memorial Library, dealing, as it does, with the subject of war, an infliction self-imposed by humanity – which at the end of this stormy century shows no signs of abating – there is plenty of folly to be pondered on. But mainly it is a record of courage, stoicism, endurance and sacrifice.

W G G
May 1999

Prefatory notes

1   This publication is both a catalogue and a bibliography. Asterisked titles have not been acquired as it goes to press. (SC = soft cover : n.d. = no date)

2   Access to the Library is open to SOAS Library card holders and is free to Burma veterans, on production of their membership cards to the Burma Star Association or any other veterans' association.

3   When there is only one copy of a title in the Library, it may not be borrowed, but can be consulted and studied in the SOAS Special Collection Reading Room. Duplicate copies of a title will normally be available for loan. It is anticipated that as a result of future additions, the number of loan copies will increase.

4   A list of books in the Japanese language is available on request to SOAS.

5   The compilers will gratefully receive information about inaccuracies and additions at the following address: Burma Campaign Library Project, 5 Beechwood Drive, Marlow, SL7 2DH.

Contents

Section A

Official Histories

Only government-sponsored publications dealing with the whole Campaign are listed here. Other publications are found under subject headings.

HISTORY OF THE SECOND WORLD WAR
THE WAR AGAINST JAPAN by S Woodburn Kirby and others

A1 Vol I The loss of Singapore 590pp 1957
A2 Vol II India's most dangerous hour 558pp 1958
A3 Vol III The decisive battles 578pp 1961
A4 Vol IV The re-conquest of Burma 583pp 1965
A5 *Vol V The surrender of Japan 622pp 1969
    HMSO illustrated maps
    Appendices to the volumes contain orders of battle of own and enemy forces, details of supply arrangements, statistics of casualties, etc.

GRAND STRATEGY

A6 *Vol III by J M A Gwyer and J R M Butler June 1941 – August 1942 416pp 1964
A7 *Vol IV by Michael Howard August 1942 – September 1943 798pp 1972
A8 *Vol V by John Ehrman August 1943 – September 1944 651pp 1956
A9 *Vol VI by John Ehrman October 1944 – August 1945 438pp 1956
    HMSO illustrated maps

OFFICIAL HISTORY OF THE INDIAN ARMED FORCES IN THE SECOND WORLD WAR

A10 *THE ROYAL INDIAN NAVY 1939 – 1945 by D J E Collins

A11 *PRASAD, Bishenwar
     RETREAT FROM BURMA 1941-1942 1953

A12 PRASAD, Bishenwar
     DEFENCE OF INDIA: POLICY AND PLANS 1963 278pp maps

AI3 *PRASAD, Bishenwar ed
EXPANSION OF THE ARMED FORCES AND DEFENCE
ORGANIZATION 1956

AI4 *MADAN
ARAKAN OPERATIONS 1942–1945 1954

AI5 PRASAD, Bishenwar ed
THE RECONQUEST OF BURMA
Vol I June 1942–June 1944 467pp illustrated maps

AI6 PRASAD, Bishenwar ed
THE RECONQUEST OF BURMA
Vol II June 1944-August 1945 539pp illustrated maps

AI7 *KHERA, P N
TECHNICAL SERVICES: I.E.M.E. AND ORDNANCE 1962

AI8 *GUPTA, S C
HISTORY OF THE INDIAN AIR FORCE 1933-1945 1961

AI9 MOUNTBATTEN, Louis, Vice-Admiral the Earl
Mountbatten of Burma
REPORT TO THE COMBINED CHIEFS OF STAFF BY THE
SUPREME ALLIED COMMANDER SOUTH-EAST ASIA
1943–1945
HMSO 1951 280pp maps
Contains list of commanders down to flotilla, brigade, group;
official reports
Plus edition published in India.
Combined Inter-Services Historical Section (India & Pakistan)

A20 *MOUNTBATTEN, Louis, Vice-Admiral the Earl
Mountbatten of Burma
POST-SURRENDER TASKS: Section E of the Report to the
Combined Chiefs of Staff by the Supreme Allied
Commander South- East Asia, 1943–45
HMSO 1969 47pp maps
The contents of this section were withheld from the main
report when it was published in 1951 as being very
politically sensitive.

Section B
General Accounts

This section comprises overviews of the Campaign.

B1   ALLEN, Louis
      BURMA: THE LONGEST WAR 1941-1945
      Dent 1984 705pp illustrated maps
      Dent 1986 705pp illustrated maps with corrections SC
      A classic account
      A Japanese translation in 3 volumes.

B2   *ANONYMOUS
      CAMPAIGN OF THE XIV ARMY 1944–1945
      (476 Indian Printing Section) [1945]

B3   *AUCHINLECK, Field Marshal Sir Claude
      DESPATCH: Operations in the Indo-Burma Theatre based on
      India from June 21, 1943 to November 15, 1943.
      (Supplement to the *London Gazette* April 27, 1948 no 38274)

B4   BHONSIE, R K
      THE JAPANESE OFFENSIVE 1941-1943: an analytical study
      New Delhi: Himalayan Books 1990 264pp SC

B5   *BOND Michelle
      THE FORGOTTEN ARMY: what were the lifestyles and
      attitudes of the soldiers of the 'Forgotten Army' fighting in
      Burma 1942-1945?
      Unpublished typescript

B6   CALLAHAN, Raymond
      BURMA 1942–1945
      Davis-Poynter 1978 190pp map

B7   *CHANDRA, Anil
      INDIAN ARMY TRIUMPHANT IN BURMA 1941–1945
      Atma Ram 1984

B8   *CHAPHEKAR, Shankarrao G
      A BRIEF STUDY OF THE BURMA CAMPAIGN 1943–1945 1955
      Poona: Maharashta Militarization Board

B9 DUPUY, Trevor N
ASIATIC LAND BATTLES: The Expansion of Japan in Asia
Franklin Watts 1963 68pp illustrated
A brief illustrated history, one of a series covering World
War II

B10 ELLIOTT, Major General J G
A ROLL OF HONOUR
Cassell 1965 394pp

B11 GURCHARAN, Maj
JAPANESE OFFENSIVE
Jalandhar: ABS publications 1990 291pp maps
Covers the period 1941-1943

B12 HICKEY, Michael
THE UNFORGETTABLE ARMY: Slim's XIVth Army in Burma
Spellmount 1992 318pp illustrated maps
Appendices list VCs awarded, order of battle etc

B13 KARAKA, D F
WITH THE 14TH ARMY
Bombay: Thacker 1944 116pp
Author was war correspondent on *The Bombay Chronicle*

B14 McKELVIE, Roy
THE WAR IN BURMA
Methuen 1948 315pp
By a military observer

B15 MASON, Philip
A MATTER OF HONOUR: an account of the Indian Army and
its men
Cape 1974 580pp illustrated maps

B16 MATTHEWS, Geoffrey
THE RE-CONQUEST OF BURMA 1943-1945
Gale & Polden 1966 115pp
A clear account written for Staff College entrants

B17 MINISTRY OF INFORMATION
SEAC SOUVENIR, PARTS ONE AND TWO
HMSO 1945 16pp and 8pp illustrated maps (photocopies)

B18 PALSOKAR, R D
BURMA: RETREAT AND RECONQUEST
Poona: the author 1974 159pp maps

B19 SLIM, William, Field Marshal the Viscount
DEFEAT INTO VICTORY
Cassell 1956 587pp illustrated maps
Four Square 1958 448pp maps SC
Masterly account of the war in Burma 1942–1945

B20 SMITH, E D
BATTLE FOR BURMA
Batsford 1979 190pp illustrated maps

B21 OWEN, Frank
THE CAMPAIGN IN BURMA
HMSO 1946 175pp illustrated maps SC
Ferozepore: English Book Depot 1952 186pp illustrated
maps
Written by Frank Owen for the Central Office of Information

B22 WAGG, Alfred
A MILLION DIED: a story of war in the Far East
Nicholson & Watson 1943 192pp

B23 WAVELL, Archibald, Field Marshal the Viscount
DESPATCH: Operations in the India Command from January
1, 1943 to June 2, 1943 16pp maps
(Supplement to the *London Gazette* April 20, 1948 no 38266)

B24 *WAVELL, Archibald, Field Marshal the Viscount
SPEECHES AND MESSAGES INDIA 1941–1943
New Delhi: Privately printed

B25 *WAVELL, Archibald, Field Marshal the Viscount
SPEECHES from October 26, 1943 to March 21, 1947
New Delhi: 152pp

B26 YEATS-BROWN, F
MARTIAL INDIA
Eyre & Spottiswoode 1945 200pp illustrated maps

Section C

The Japanese Invasion

Individual experiences of these events can be found under PERSONAL NARRATIVES *Section M*.

C1 BARNARD, Jack
THE HUMP: the greatest untold history of the war
Souvenir Press 1960 192pp illustrated

C2 BELDEN, Jack
RETREAT WITH STILWELL
New York: Knopf 1943 368pp map

C3 BURCHETT, W G
BOMBS OVER BURMA
Melbourne: F W Cheshire 1944 260pp illustrated map

C4 BURCHETT, W G
TREK BACK FROM BURMA
India: Allahabad n.d. 330pp

C5 CAREW, Tim
THE LONGEST RETREAT: the Burma Campaign 1942
Hamish Hamilton 1969 288pp illustrated maps

C6 CARMICHAEL, Pat R D
MOUNTAIN BATTERY
Devin Books 1983 246pp illustrated maps

C7 CHRISTIAN, John L
BURMA AND THE JAPANESE INVADER
Bombay: Thacker 1945 418pp

C8 DILLON, Terence
RANGOON TO KOHIMA
Gloucester Regiment 148pp

C9 DORN, Frank
WALK OUT WITH STILWELL IN BURMA
New York: Thomas Y Crowell 1971 258pp illustrated maps

C10 DRAPER, Alfred
DAWNS LIKE THUNDER: the retreat from Burma 1942
Leo Cooper 1987 301pp illustrated maps

C11 FINNERTY, John
ALL QUIET ON THE IRRAWADDY
New Horizon 1979 225pp illustrated

C12 FINNERTY, John
ALL HELL ON THE IRRAWADDY
Anchor Publications 1985 286pp illustrated

C13 GALLAGHER, O D
RETREAT IN THE EAST
Harrap 1942 190pp illustrated

C14 GARDINER, John Ronald (Ritchie)
DIARY OF A JOURNEY FROM SUMPRABUM TO MARGHERITA
BY THE CHAUKKAN PASS May-July 1942
Unpublished n.d. 188pp map (typescript)

C15 GRANT, Ian Lyall and TAMAYAMA
BURMA 1942: THE JAPANESE INVASION – both sides tell the
story of a savage jungle war
Zampi Press 1999 350pp illustrated maps

C16 GRIBBLE, R H
OUT OF THE BURMA NIGHT: being the fantastic journey
through the wilderness of the Hukawng Valley ... at the time
of the Japanese invasion of Burma
Calcutta: Thacker & Spink 1944 164pp illustrated

C17 *KNIGHT, Allan
ESCAPE FROM THE YELLOW PERIL: personal experiences of an
evacuee from Burma
India Allahabad: Kitab Mahal 1945 91pp

C18 LACKERSTEEN, D
DIAMONDS IN THE DUST
Kitabistan: Invasion 1942 49pp

C19 LEASOR, James
THE MARINE FROM MANDALAY
Leo Cooper 1991 146pp

C20 LUNT, James
A HELL OF A LICKING: the retreat from Burma 1941-1942
Collins 1986 318 pp illustrated maps
David & Charles 1986 319pp illustrated maps SC

C21 McCRAE, Alistair
IRRAWADDY FLOTILLA
James Paton 1978

C22 MacFETRIDGE, Charles
THE BATTLE OF SHWEGYIN May 10, 1942
Unpublished 8pp typescript map

C23 MACKENZIE, Compton
EASTERN EPIC Vol 1 September 1939 – March 1943: Defence
Chatto & Windus 1951 646 pp maps

C24 MAINS, Tony
THE RETREAT FROM BURMA: an intelligence officer's
personal story
Foulsham 1973 152pp illustrated map

C25 MALGONKAR, Manohar
DISTANT DRUM
Bombay: Asia Publishing House 1960 257pp

C26 *RUSSELL, Stanley F
MUDDY EXODUS: a story of the evacuation of Burma 1942
Epworth 1943 64pp

C27 *SINGH, Bishan
BURMA RETREAT
India: Kanpur: Vasuder Singh 1949

C28 SMYTH, John
BEFORE THE DAWN: a story of two historic retreats
Cassell 1957 235pp illustrated maps
Dunkirk: 1940 Burma: 1942
Author commanded 17 Indian Division

C29 STEWART, Adrian
THE UNDERRATED ENEMY: Britain's War with Japan
December 1941 – May 1942
Kimber 1987 234pp illustrated maps

C30 TAINSH, A R
... AND SOME FELL BY THE WAYSIDE: an account of the North
Burma evacuation
Bombay: Orient Longmans 1950 182pp illustrated map

C31 TINKER, Hugh
THE INDIA EXODUS FROM BURMA 1942 in
Journal of South-East Asian Studies 1975

C32 TYSON, Geoffrey
FORGOTTEN FRONTIER
Calcutta: Targett 1945 illustrated maps
Tea planters of North-East India during the retreat

C33 *WAVELL, Archibald, Field Marshal the Viscount
DESPATCH: Operation in the Eastern Theatre, based on
India, from March 1942 to December 31, 1942
(Supplement to the *London Gazette* September 17, 1946
no 37728)

C34 WAVELL, Archibald, Field Marshal the Viscount
DESPATCH: Operations in Burma from December 15, 1941
to May 20, 1942 (covering reports by Lieut-General
T J Hutton and General the Hon Sir Harold Alexander) 46pp
(Supplement to the *London Gazette* March 5, 1948
no 38228)

Section D
Arakan

Accounts of the Arakan front from 1942 to 1945.
References to Arakan experiences can be found in *Sections
A, B, C, K, L* and *M*.

D1 *ANONYMOUS
HISTORY OF THE ARAKAN CAMPAIGN 1944–1945
HQ XV Indian Corps [1946?]

D2 ANONYMOUS
THE STORY OF THE 25TH INDIAN DIVISION: the Arakan
campaign
Bombay: Government of India War Department n.d. 37pp
illustrated SC

D3 ANONYMOUS
ARAKAN ASSIGNMENT: the story of the 82nd West African
Division
West Africa: P R Services n.d. 44pp illustrated map SC

D4 BOWEN, C G
WEST AFRICAN WAY: the story of the Burma Campaign
1943–1945 5th Bn Gold Coast Regt
Privately published n.d. Various paginations map
(photocopy)

D5 CATTANACH, John
THE JEEP TRACK: the story of the 81st West African Division
fighting on the Arakan front in Burma
Regency Press 1990 79pp

D6 *CLARKE, Michael S
KALADAN MORTARS: a walk on the knife edge
Woodfield Publishing 1994 93pp illustrated maps SC
A West African mortar battery in the Kaladan Valley
1944–1945

D7 *EMMET, A Maitland
THE ARAKAN CAMPAIGN OF THE 25TH INDIAN DIVISION
March 1944 – March 1945
1946 131pp

D8 FULLER, A R and LEWENDON
7TH INDIAN FIELD REGT ROYAL INDIAN ARTILLERY: a
narrative 1943–1947
Privately published 1996 Various pagination illustrated
maps SC
7th and 26th Indian Divisions in Arakan

D9 JEFFREYS, P J
BURMA 1943–1944: memories of the First Kaladan
Campaign 81st (West African) Division
Privately published 53pp illustrated map (photocopy) m/s

D10 JEFFREYS, P J
BURMA 1944–1945: memories of the Second Kaladan
Campaign 5th (West African Brigade) 81st (West African)
Division
Privately published 28pp illustrated map (photocopy) m/s

D11 PHILLIPS, C E Lucas
THE RAIDERS OF ARAKAN
Heinemann 1971 198pp illustrated maps
Royal Marines Commandoes, West African and V Force
activity 1943–1944

D12 STRAUBENZEE, Philip van
DESERT, JUNGLE AND DALE: A MEMOIR
Pentland Press 1991 140pp illustrated maps
Author was CO 1st Bn The Sierra Leone Regt 1944–1945
82nd (West African) Division

D13 SWYNNERTON, Charles R A
A SHORT HISTORY OF THE 1ST (WEST AFRICAN) INFANTRY
BRIGADE IN THE ARAKAN 1944–1945
2nd ed Lagos 1949 95pp maps
Author was the Brigade Commander

D14 TURNBULL, Patrick
THE BATTLE OF THE BOX
Ian Allan 1979 144pp illustrated maps
The decisive engagement

D15 WILMOT, Alec
27TH RA – ONLY JUNGLE AND THE JAPANESE
The author 1998 166pp illustrated SC
A Field Regiment in 26th Indian Division,
March 1944 – August 1945

Section E

Assam, Manipur and the advance to Mandalay and Rangoon

E1 ALLEN, Louis
SITTANG THE LAST BATTLE: the end of the Japanese in Burma
July – August 1945
Military Book Society 1973 284pp illustrated maps

E2 ANONYMOUS
40TH ANNIVERSARY BATTLE OF KOHIMA
Illustrated leaflet 8pp

E3 ATKINS, David
THE RELUCTANT MAJOR
Toat Press 1986 110pp illustrated map
RIASC Transport Company

E4 ATKINS, David
THE FORGOTTEN MAJOR
Toat Press 1989 145pp illustrated maps
300 Indian GPT Company

E5 BARKER, A J
THE MARCH ON DELHI
Faber 1963 302pp illustrated maps
Dehradun: Netaji Publishing 1990

E6 BOND, Brian ed
FALLEN STARS: eleven studies of 20th century military
disasters
Brasseys (UK) 1991 272pp maps
Contains *Mutaguchi Renya and the invasion of India* by
Louis Allen 25pp

E7 BOWER, Ursula Graham
NAGA PATH
Murray 1950 260pp illustrated map

E8   CAMPBELL, Arthur
THE SIEGE: A STORY FROM KOHIMA
Allen & Unwin 1956 212pp illustrated maps
Corgi 1957 251pp maps SC

E9   COLVIN, John
NO ORDINARY MEN: the story of the battle of Kohima
Leo Cooper 1995 263pp illustrated maps

E10   CROSS, J P
JUNGLE WARFARE: EXPERIENCES AND ENCOUNTERS
Guild Publishing 1989 222pp illustrated

E11   EVANS, Geoffrey and BRETT-JAMES
IMPHAL: A FLOWER ON LOFTY HEIGHTS
Macmillan 1962 348pp illustrated maps

E12   FREER, Arthur F
NUNSHIGUM: ON THE ROAD TO MANDALAY
Pentland Press 1995 262pp maps
Tank action by 3rd Carabiniers north of Imphal
April 1944

E13   GIFFARD, General Sir George
DESPATCH: Operations in Burma and North East India
from November 16, 1943 to June 22, 1944 31pp map
Maps for use with Army and Air Despatches of the Burma
Campaign
(Supplement to the *London Gazette* March 13, 1951
no 39171)

E14   GIFFARD, General Sir George
DESPATCH: Operations in Assam and Burma June 23, 1944
to November 12, 1944 27pp map
(Supplement to the *London Gazette* March 30, 1951
no 39187)

E15   *GOVERNMENT OF INDIA WAR DEPARTMENT
ON TO RANGOON
Bombay: Claridge 1945

E16 GRANT, Ian Lyall
BURMA: THE TURNING POINT: the seven battles on the Tiddim
Road ...
Zampi Press 1993 255pp illustrated maps

E17 HAWKINS, V F S
OPERATIONS OF THE 5TH INFANTRY BRIGADE, 2 DIVISION, in
Assam March 30 – May 12, 1944 with special reference to
the Battle of Kohima
Unpublished typescript n.d. 125pp

E18 KENDALL, Bill
I WAS THERE! WITH THE BRITISH 2ND DIVISION
The author 60pp SC

E19 KING-CLARK, R
THE BATTLE FOR KOHIMA: the narrative of the 2nd Battalion
the Manchester Regiment, the Machine Gun battalion of the
British 2nd Division
Fleur de Lys Publishing 1995 138pp illustrated maps SC

E20 *LEESE, General Sir Oliver
DESPATCH: Operations in Burma from November 12, 1944
to August 15, 1945
(Supplement to the *London Gazette* April 6, 1951 no 39195)

E21 McCANN, John
KOHIMA – AN HISTORIC VILLAGE AND OTHER SHORT STORIES
The author 401pp illustrated SC
The author served in 1/8th Lancashire Fusiliers

E22 McCANN, John
ECHOES OF KOHIMA
The author 1989 416pp illustrated SC

E23 *McCANN, John
RETURN TO KOHIMA
The author 1993

E24 NEILD, Eric
COLLECTION of papers, correspondence, extracts on the
BATTLE AT SANGSHAK, 50th Indian Parachute Brigade etc

E25 PHILLIPS, C E Lucas
Springboard to victory: battle for Kohima
Heinemann 1966 242pp illustrated maps
Delhi: Army Publishers n.d.

E26 *ROONEY, David
Burma Victory: Imphal, Kohima and the Chindit issue
March 1944 to May 1945
Arms and Armour Press 1992 208pp illustrated maps

E27 SEAMAN, Harry
The Battle at Sangshak: Burma, March 1944
Leo Cooper 1989 148pp illustrated maps
The prelude to Kohima

E28 SMITH, W C
The Unsung Heroes: a personal account
The author 1995 98pp sc

E29 SWINSON, Arthur
Kohima
Cassell 1966 275pp illustrated maps
Arrow Books 1968 320pp illustrated maps sc

E30 WAVELL, Archibald, Field Marshal the Viscount
Confidential directive 'To officers of India Command'
GHQ Delhi May 22, 1943 6pp typescript

E31 *WILSON, Richard C
The Imphal Shrimps
Chester: the author 1962

E32 *WILSON, Richard C
Tailpiece at Tamu
Chester: the author 1962

Section F

China-Burma-India Theatre and the Burma Road

Concerns operations in North Burma and in China, mainly by US and Chinese forces. Books on General Stilwell will be found under BIOGRAPHIES *Section L*. 'The Hump' – air transport between India, North Burma and China is included in THE WAR IN THE AIR *Section U*.

F1   ADAMSON, Iain
THE FORGOTTEN MEN
Bell 1965 195pp
A British Commando training mission to China

F2   ANONYMOUS
MERRILL'S MARAUDERS
NY: Peducah Pub 1987 122pp illustrated

F3   BAKER, Alan
MERRILL'S MARAUDERS
Pan/Ballantine 1972 160pp illustrated maps SC

F4   BATES, Richard F
MEMORIES OF MILITARY SERVICE: a teenager in Burma
The author 1995 178pp illustrated maps

F5   BELDEN, Jack
STILL TIME TO DIE
Gollanz 1945 288pp

F6   BONHAM, Frank
BURMA RIFLES: a story of Merrill's Marauders
New York: Crowell 1960 260pp

F7   BRADLEY, Neville
THE OLD BURMA ROAD: a journey on foot and muleback
Heinemann 1945 138pp illustrated
1930

F8 CHAN, Won-loy
BURMA: THE UNTOLD STORY
Novato, CA: Presidio [1986?] 149pp illustrated

F9 CHIANG YEE
THE MEN OF THE BURMA ROAD
Methuen 3rd ed 1942 88pp illustrated

F10 *CHUONG, Tong-Guk
BURMA-YUNNAN VICTORY IN CHINA'S 8TH WAR 1945

F11 COE, Douglas
BURMA ROAD
New York: Julian Messner 1946 192pp illustrated map

F12 ELDRIDGE, Fred
WRATH IN BURMA: the uncensored story of General Stilwell
and international manoeuvres in the Far East
New York: Doubleday 1946 320pp illustrated maps

F13 ELLIOTT-BATEMAN, Michael
DEFEAT IN THE EAST: the mark of Mao Tse-tung on war
Oxford 1967 270pp

F14 FELLOWES-GORDON, Ian
THE MAGIC WAR: the battle for North Burma
New York: Scribner's 1971 180pp illustrated maps

F15 FISCHER, Edward
THE CHANCY WAR: winning in China, Burma and India in
World War Two
New York: Orion Books 1991 250pp illustrated maps

F16 GEORGE, John B
SHOTS FIRED IN ANGER: A rifleman's view of the war in the
Pacific ...with Merrill's Marauders
Washington DC National Rifle Association of America
2nd ed 1991 535pp illustrated maps
Book I Guadalcanal Book II Burma

F17 *GEREN, Paul Francis
BURMA DIARY

Deland, Florida: Everett/Edwards Presentation edition 1968
63pp

F18 *GLASS, S A
WHO STOLE MY MULE?
Maysville, Kentucky: Bell Enterprises [1985?]
An American with Northern Combat Command

F19 *HERMAN, Leonard
BURMA MISSION: COMPANY D
Allentown, Pennsylvania: the author 1946

F20 *HIROSHI, Fowa
JAPANESE OPERATIONS IN THE HUKAWNG VALLEY
USA: Military Review 1963

F21 HO, Yng-Ch'i
THE BIG CIRCLE
New York: Exposition Press 1948 152pp
The role of Chinese forces in the Burmese Campaigns of the
Second World War

F22 HOYT, Edwin P
MERRILL'S MARAUDERS
Los Angeles: Pinnacle Books 1980 148pp SC

F23 *HUNTER, Charles Newton
GALAHAD
San Antonio, Texas: The Naylor Company 1963 233pp
illustrated maps
Galahad – the code name for the US long range penetration
group in CBI

F24 *KADEL, Bob
'WHERE I CAME IN' IN CHINA-BURMA-INDIA
Paducah, Kentucky: Turner Publishing 1987

F25 *LAURET, Jean-Claude
FORCES SPECIALES EN BIRMANIE: 1944 Les Mauraudeurs de
Merrill
Paris: Presses de la Cite 1986 285 illustrated map
In French

F26 OGBURN, Charlton
THE MARAUDERS
New York: Harper 1959 307pp illustrated map
Quality Book Club 1960 319pp map

F27 PEERS, William and BRELIS
BEHIND THE BURMA ROAD
Robert Hale 1964 194pp illustrated maps

F28 PHILIPS, Bob
KC8 BURMA
Manhattan, Kansas: Sunflower University Press 1992
194pp illustrated map SC
KC8 was a CBI Air Warning Team

F29 *RANDOLPH, John H
MARSMEN IN BURMA
Houston, Texas: the author 1946

F30 ROMANUS, Charles F and SUNDERLAND
THE UNITED STATES ARMY IN WORLD WAR II: China-Burma-
India Theater 3 volumes:
Stilwell's Mission to China 441pp
Stilwell's Command problems 515pp
Time runs out in CBI 428pp
Washington DC: Office of the Chief of Military History:
Department of The Army 1953-1956-1959 illustrated maps

F31 SAMSON, G
BURMA ROAD: report of an address
China Society 1949

F32 SLATER, Robert
GUNS THROUGH ARCADY: Burma and the Burma Road
Sydney: Angus & Robertson 1941 239pp illustrated
A pre-war account to 1939

F33 SMITH, Nicol
BURMA ROAD
Indianapolis: Bobbs-Merrill 1940 333pp

F34 *STILWELL, Joseph
The Campaign in Burma March/June 1942
Unpublished

F35 STILWELL, Joseph
The Stilwell papers, arranged and edited by Theodore H
White
MacDonald 1949 327pp illustrated maps

F36 *STILWELL, Joseph
History of the CBI Theatre
(Stilwell's Personal File B1 1942–1944) Scholarly Resources

F37 STOWE, Leland
They shall not sleep
New York: Knopf 1944 424pp

F38 TAN, Pei-Ying
The Building of the Burma Road
New York: McGraw-Hill 1945 204pp illustrated map

F39 TAYMAN, Nelson-Grant
Stilwell Road – land route to China 18pp illustrated SC
(Article in *National Geographic Magazine* Vol LXXXVII
no 6, June 1945)

F40 *TYSON, Geoffrey
Ramgarh 'Now it can be told'
US Army: Ramgarh Training Center, CBI 1945

F41 *TYSON, Geoffrey
American forces in action: Merrill's Marauders
Center of Military History 1990

F42 *UNITED STATES WAR DEPARTMENT
Merrill's Marauders February – May 1944
Washington DC: War Department Historical Division

F43 *WILLIAMS, Robert P
One Man's CBI
Unpublished

Section G

The Chindits

Biographies of Orde Wingate can be found in *Section L*.

G1 *AIR MINISTRY
Operation 'Thursday' Allied landings in N E Burma

G2 *ALISON, J R
Chindit operation in Burma
Rand Corporation 1943 1963

G3 BAGGALEY, James
A Chindit story
Souvenir Press 1954 163pp map
Panther 1958 158pp SC

G4 BIDWELL, Shelford
The Chindit war: the campaign in Burma 1944
Hodder & Stoughton 1979 304pp illustrated maps
New York: Macmillan 1979
The standard account

G5 BOYLE, Patrick and MUSGRAVE-WOOD
Jungle, jungle, little Chindit
Hollis & Carter [1946?] 97pp illustrated
Humorous

G6 BURCHETT, W G
Wingate's phantom army
Bombay: Thacker 1944 240pp illustrated map

G7 BURCHETT, W G
Wingate adventure
Melbourne: F W Cheshire 1944 188pp illustrated map

G8 BUTT, Paul Le
We too can die: tales of the Chindits
Robert Anscombe 1947 163pp

G9 CALVERT, Michael
PRISONERS OF HOPE
Cape 1952 303pp illustrated maps
Corgi Books 1973 320pp illustrated maps SC
(With a new postscript by the author)

G10 CALVERT, Mike
FIGHTING MAD
Airlife 1996 208pp illustrated

G11 CALVERT, Michael
CHINDITS: LONG RANGE PENETRATION
Pan Ballantine n.d. 159pp illustrated maps SC

G12 CARFRAE, Charles
CHINDIT COLUMN
William Kimber 1985 194pp illustrated maps
7th Bn The Nigeria Regiment during the Second
Chindit operation

G13 CHARGE, Des
THE BEGINNING OF THE END: a story about the
Chindits in Burma
Newton 1995 illustrated map

G14 CHINDITS O C A UK
MAJOR GENERAL O C WINGATE DSO: an appreciation ...
For private circulation 89pp SC

G15 CHINNERY, Philip D
MARCH OR DIE: the story of Wingate's Chindits
Airlife 1997 256pp illustrated maps

G16 DENNY, J H
CHINDIT INDISCRETION
Christopher Johnson 1956 256pp port maps
Panther 1956 SC

G17 FERGUSSON, Bernard
BEYOND THE CHINDWIN: being an account of the
adventures of Number Five Column of the Wingate
expedition into Burma 1943

Collins 1945 255pp illustrated maps
Collins: St James's Library series 1951 × 2
Anthony Mott: The War Library 1983

G18 FERGUSSON, Bernard
THE WILD GREEN EARTH
Collins 1946 228pp maps
The author commanded 16th Brigade in the Second
Chindit operation

G19 HALLEY, David
WITH WINGATE IN BURMA
Wm Hodge 1945 189pp map

G20 HASKINS, P C
EPIC IN NAGALAND 10pp
A CHINDIT OPERATION 25pp
Unpublished n.d. SC

G21 HILL, George
OH! TO BE A CHINDIT
Unpublished n.d. 52pp SC

G22 JAMES, Harold
ACROSS THE THRESHOLD OF BATTLE: behind Japanese
lines with Wingate's Chindits Burma 1943
Book Guild 1993 250pp illustrated maps

G23 JAMES, Richard Rhodes
CHINDIT
Sphere 1981 214pp maps SC
John Murray 1980 224pp illustrated maps

G24 JEFFREY, W F
SUNBEAMS LIKE SWORDS
Hodder & Stoughton 1950 176pp

G25 MACHORTON, Ian
SAFER THAN A KNOWN WAY: one man's epic struggle against
Japanese and jungle
Popular Book Club 1958 248pp illustrated map

G26 MACKAY, Donald
A PADRE WITH THE CHINDITS
Reproduced from *The Covenanter* the Regimental Journal
of the Cameronians 1960 13pp

G27 MILNER, Joe
TO BLAZES WITH GLORY: a Chindit's war
Edward Gaskell, The Lazarus Press 1995 475pp illustrated
maps

G28 O'BRIEN, Terence
OUT OF THE BLUE: a pilot with the Chindits
Collins 1984 272pp map

G29 ROLO, Charles J
WINGATE'S RAIDERS
Harrap 1946 199pp illustrated

G30 ROSSETTO, Luigi
MAJOR-GENERAL ORDE WINGATE AND THE DEVELOPMENT
OF LONG-RANGE PENETRATION
Manhattan, Kansas: MA/AH Publishing – Sunflower
University Press 1982 471pp maps

G31 SHARPE, Philip
TO BE A CHINDIT
Book Guild 1995 273pp illustrated maps

G32 SHAW, James
THE MARCH OUT
Hart-Davis 1953 206pp illustrated map

G33 SHAW, Jesse
SPECIAL FORCE: A CHINDIT'S STORY
Alan Sutton 1986 271pp illustrated
12th Bn The Nigeria Regt during the Second Chindit
operation 1944

G34 SHIRREFF, David
WINGATE'S ADC CAPTAIN G H BORROW MC
Unpublished typescript 8pp n.d. SC

G35 STIBBE, Philip
RETURN VIA RANGOON: a young Chindit survives the jungle
and Japanese captivity
Leo Cooper 1994 247pp map
No 5 Column 1943 Chindit operation

G36 SMYTHIES, B E
DIARY
Unpublished 32pp n.d. maps
Author was Civil Affairs Officer 16 Inf Bde

G37 SYMES, G W
SOME VIEWS OF THE WINGATE EXPEDITIONS OF 1943 AND
1944 FROM THE JAPANESE STANDPOINT
Unpublished 1946 4pp
The result of interrogation of Japanese staff officers by
Major General Symes

G38 THOMAS, Lowell
BACK TO MANDALAY
Shakespeare Head 1952 255pp illustrated

G39 THOMPSON, Robert
MAKE FOR THE HILLS: memories of Far Eastern Wars
Leo Cooper 1989 233pp illustrated maps
An RAF officer in both Chindit operations
First seventy-six pages deal with Burma

G40 *THOMPSON, Robert and MEAD
JUDGMENT ON WINGATE
Article *Army Quarterly* July 1978

G41 TOWILL, Bill
A CHINDIT'S CHRONICLE
Privately published [1990?] 143pp

G42 *WHYTE, Desmond
A TRYING CHINDIT
(*British Medical Journal* December 18–25, 1982 pp1776–9)

G43 WILCOX, W A
CHINDIT COLUMN 76
Calcutta: Longmans 1945 137pp illustrated maps

Section H

Clandestine Operations

Secret operations conducted by irregular forces in enemy country.

H1 *ATHERTON, Louise
SOE: OPERATIONS IN THE FAR EAST
An introductory guide to the newly-released records of the SOE in the Public Record Office 1997

H2 *GUAR, Dharmendra
BEHIND THE ENEMY LINES
New Delhi: Sterling 1975

H3 HISTORY OF THE SECOND WORLD WAR
British intelligence in the Second World War
Vol 5 by Michael Howard
HMSO 1990 271pp maps
pp 203–222 deal with the Far East 1942–1945

H4 BEAMISH, John
BURMA DROP
Elek Books 1958 illustrated map
Z force

H5 BOWEN, John
UNDERCOVER IN THE JUNGLE
Kimber 1978 206pp illustrated maps
V force

H6 BRAUND, H E W
THREE YEARS WITH THE CHIN LEVIES
United Services Institution of India 17pp map
Photocopy of pamphlet

H7 CRUICKSHANK, Charles
SOE IN THE FAR EAST
Oxford University Press 1983 285pp illustrated map SC
Special Operations Executive

H8 DUNLOP, Richard
BEHIND JAPANESE LINES WITH THE OSS IN BURMA
Chicago: Rand McNally 1979 448pp illustrated maps
The CBI theatre

H9 EVANS, Lieut-General Sir Geoffrey
THE JOHNNIES
Cassell 1964 231pp illustrated maps
Commissioned Forestry Officers leading Karens, Chins,
Kachins in Z force

H10 FELLOWES-GORDON, Ian
AMIABLE ASSASSINS: the story of the Kachin guerrillas of
North Burma
Hale 1957 illustrated

H11 FELLOWES-GORDON, Ian
THE BATTLE FOR NAW SENG'S KINGDOM: General Stilwell's
North Burma campaign and its aftermath
Leo Cooper 1971 176pp illustrated maps
The Kachin Levies

H12 *GRAHAM, W Gordon
V FORCE HISTORY
GHQ New Delhi 1945

H13 GUTHRIE, D
JUNGLE DIARY
Macmillan 1946 127pp illustrated

H14 HAMOND, Robert
THE FLAME OF FREEDOM: Corporal Pagani's escape from the
railway of Death
Leo Cooper 1988
He reached Burma and joined the Karen resistance

H15 HEILBRUNN, Otto
WARFARE IN THE ENEMY'S REAR
Praeger 1963 231pp maps

H16 HILSMAN, Roger
AMERICAN GUERRILLA: my war behind Japanese lines
Washington: Brassey's (US) 1990 300pp

H17 IWAICHI, Fujiwara
F KIKAN: JAPANESE ARMY INTELLIGENCE OPERATIONS IN
SOUTHEAST ASIA DURING WORLD WAR II
Hong Kong: Heinemann Asia 1983 368pp illustrated maps

H18 IRWIN, Anthony
BURMESE OUTPOST
Collins 1945 160pp illustrated maps
V force in Arakan

H19 LEASOR, James
BOARDING PARTY: The last action of the Calcutta Light Force
1st ed 1978
Heinemann 204pp
Sabotage of German ship anchored in Neutral waters on
West Coast of India

H20 MAINS, Tony
FIELD SECURITY: VERY ORDINARY INTELLIGENCE
Picton 1992 181pp SC

H21 MOON, Thomas N and EIFLER
THE DEADLIEST COLONEL
New York: Vantage Press 1975 342pp illustrated
Colonel Eifler commanded an office of Strategic Services
Detachment in Northern Burma

H22 MORRISON, Ian
GRANDFATHER LONGLEGS: the life and gallant death of
Major H P Seagrim GC DSO MBE
Faber & Faber 1947 239pp illustrated map
Service with the Karen levies behind the Japanese lines

H23 O'BRIEN, Terence
THE MOONLIGHT WAR: the story of clandestine operations
in Southeast Asia 1944–1945
Collins 1987 363pp map

H24 STRIPP, Alan
CODEBREAKER IN THE FAR EAST
Oxford University Press 1995 204pp illustrated map SC

H25 TAYLOR, C G
THE FORGOTTEN ONE OF SEAC AND FORCE 136
A H Stockwell 1989 88pp

Section I

Civilian Burma

Books about Burma just before, during and after the
Japanese occupation.

I I *HISTORY OF THE SECOND WORLD WAR
CIVIL AFFAIRS AND MILITARY GOVERNMENT SERIES –
BRITISH MILITARY ADMINISTRATION IN THE FAR EAST
1943–1946
by F S V Dennison
HMSO 1956 483pp maps

I 2 ANONYMOUS
POCKET GUIDE TO BURMA
Pamphlet 57pp

I 3 ANONYMOUS
BURMA TODAY Vol I I No 8
Pamphlet 12pp

I 4 *APPLETON, George
BURMA SPG (The War and after series)
1945 44pp illustrated
Author was Archdeacon of Rangoon and Director of Public
Relations Government of Burma, 1944–46. He summarises
the Japanese invasion and the recapture of Burma with
emphasis on the role of the Christian Church.

I 5 APPLETON, George
BUDDISM IN BURMA
Longmans 49pp Pamphlet

I 6 APPLETON, George
BURMA RICE
Longmans 32pp Pamphlet

I 7 APPLETON, George
THREE MONTHS HARD LABOUR
Burma Christian Literature Society 64pp Pamphlet

1 8   ARNOLD, Sue
A BURMESE LEGACY
Hodder & Stoughton 1996 210pp map
Author visits her Anglo-Burmese family

1 9   AUCKLAND, R G compiler
CATALOGUE OF LEAFLETS DROPPED OVER BURMESE
CIVILIANS 1942–1945 produced by Political Warfare
Directorate and SEAC
Leeds: Psywar 1991 8pp

1 10 BANERJEE, Anil Chandra
ANNEXATION OF BURMA
A Mukherjee & Bros 1944 338pp

1 11 BA MAW, U
BREAKTHROUGH IN BURMA: memoirs of a revolution
1939–1944
New Haven: Yale University Press 1968 483pp ports maps

1 12 BAIRD-MURRAY, Maureen
A WORLD OVERTURNED: a Burmese childhood 1933–1947
Constable 1997 190pp illustrated map

1 13 BECKA, Jack
THE NATIONAL LIBERATION MOVEMENT IN BURMA DURING
THE JAPANESE OCCUPATION PERIOD 1941–1945
Prague: Oriental Institute in Academia 1983 387pp

1 14 BRAUND, H E W
CALLING TO MIND: being some account of the first hundred
years (1870–1970) of Steel Brothers & Company Limited
Pergamon 1975 151pp illustrated maps
Established in Rangoon, the company had extensive interests
in rice, oil and forestry

1 15 BRAUND, Harold
DISTINCTLY I REMEMBER: a personal story of Burma
Australia: Mount Eliza: Wren Publishing 1972 296pp
illustrated maps
A civilian service with Steel Brothers and military service
with the Chin levies

1 16 BURMA, Government of
BURMA HANDBOOK
Simla: Government of India Press 1944 126pp maps

1 17 BURMA INTELLIGENCE BUREAU
BURMA DURING THE JAPANESE OCCUPATION, authorized by
the Governor of Burma
Simla 1943–1944 2 vols maps

1 18 CHIT, Myo Khin
THREE YEARS UNDER THE JAPS 1945
1945 46pp

1 19 CHRISTIAN, John L
BURMA
London: Collins 176pp

1 20 COLLIS, Maurice
LAST AND FIRST IN BURMA
Faber 1956 303pp illustrated

1 21 CORPE, Hilda R
PRISONER BEYOND THE CHINDWIN
Arthur Barker 1955 158pp illustrated

1 22 EVACUEE
HOW TO SPEAK BURMESE
Thacker & Co Ltd 78pp

1 23 FERGUSSON, D H
A LOST CITY IN BURMA
The Rampart Library No 48, Thacker 104pp

1 24 FERRIER, A J
THE CARE & MANAGEMENT OF ELEPHANTS IN BURMA
Steel Bros & Co 177pp illustrated

1 25 *FISCHER, Edward
MISSION IN BURMA: Columban Fathers forty-three years in
Kachin Country
New York: The Seabury Press 1980 170pp illustrated map
Covers the work of the fifty-one Columban Fathers working

as missionaries in Upper Burma 1936–1979 including
particularly their experiences of the War, OSS, etc.

1 26 FOUCAR, E C V
I Lived in Burma
Dobson 1956 272pp illustrated
A lawyer in Burma from 1922, during the Retreat, and
return to Burma after victory

1 27 FOUCAR, E C V
They reigned in Mandalay
Dobson 1946 165pp illustrated

1 28 GLASS, Leslie
The Changing of kings: memories of Burma 1934–1949
Peter Owen 1985 241pp

1 29 GREENWOOD, Nicholas (compiler)
Shades of gold and green: anecdotes of colonial Burmah
1886–1948
New Delhi: Asian Educational Services 1998 307pp
illustrated map
Civilian Burma before the occupation

1 30 HARVEY, G E
British Rule in Burma 1924–1942
Faber & Faber 100pp

1 31 HASKINS, F
Burma yesterday & tomorrow
The Rampart Library No 57 Thacker 94pp

1 32 *HEARSEY, May
Land of Chindits and rubies
M A Leverston-Allen 1982 220pp
Author is Anglo-Burmese and describes life before, during
and after the War in Burma.

1 33 *HIA, Pe
The Japanese occupation of Burma
Ithaca 1961

I 34 INDIA Directorate of Army Education
BURMA DURING THE WAR 1945
12pp SC
Current affairs pamphlet

I 35 JESSE, F Tennyson
THE STORY OF BURMA
Macmillan 1946 219pp illustrated maps
567 BC to AD 1945

I 36 LEWIS, Norman
GOLDEN EARTH: travels in Burma
Jonathan Cape 1952 279pp illustrated map

I 37 McCRAE, Alistair (compiler)
TALES OF BURMA
James Paton 1981 168pp illustrated map SC
Nine contributors

I 38 McENERY, John H
EPILOGUE IN BURMA 1945–1948: the military dimension of
British withdrawal
Spellmount 1990 160pp illustrated map

I 39 MANNIN, Ethel
LAND OF THE CRESTED LION: a journey through modern
Burma
Jarrolds 1955 256pp illustrated map

I 40 MAYBURY, Maurice
HEAVEN-BORN IN BURMA
Folio Hadspen 1984–1986 3 volumes illustrated maps
Vol 1 The Daily round 184pp
Vol 2 Flight of the heaven-born 180pp
Vol 3 Swan-song of the heaven-born 244pp
The period 1939–1948

I 41 MI MI KHAING
BURMESE FAMILY
Bloomington: Indiana University Press 1962 200pp
illustrated

142 MOREHEAD, F T
THE FORESTS OF BURMA
Longmans 66pp Pamphlet

143 NU, Thakin U
BURMA UNDER THE JAPANESE: pictures and portraits
Macmillan 1954 160pp illustrated
Author was Prime Minister 1947–1962

144 PEARN, B R
BURMA BACKGROUND
Longmans 44pp Pamphlet

145 RATTENBURY, Harold B
CHINA-BURMA VAGABOND
Travel Book Club 1948 280pp

146 RILLSTONE, Rev Thomas
... AND BEHOLD WE LIVE
St Columban's Mission Society 114pp
A missionary's experiences during the Japanese occupation

147 SEIN, Mamya
BURMA
Oxford University Press 1943 32pp
Pamphlet

148 *SMITH, Martin
BURMA: INSURGENCY AND THE POLITICS OF ETHNICITY
Zed Books 1991 492pp

149 SPATE, O H K
BURMA SETTING
Longmans 34pp Pamphlet

150 STEVENSON, H N C
THE HILL PEOPLES OF BURMA
Longmans 50pp Pamphlet

151 TAYLOR, Robert H
MARXISM AND RESISTANCE IN BURMA 1942–1945: Thein Pe
Myint's Wartime traveller
Athens: Ohio University Press 1984 326pp illustrated maps

I 52 THEIN Pe Myint
WHAT HAPPENED IN BURMA: the frank revelations of a
young Burmese revolutionary leader who escaped from
Burma to India
Allahabad: Kitabistan 1943

I 53 THOMPSON, Edward
BURMESE SILVER
Faber & Faber 1944 216pp

I 54 THORP, Ellen
QUIET SKIES ON SALWEEN
Jonathan Cape,1945 175pp

I 55 TRAGER, Frank N ed
BURMA: Japanese Military Administration selected
documents 1941–1945
Philadelphia: University of Pennsylvania Press 1971 279pp

I 56 TINKER, Hugh ed
BURMA THE STRUGGLE FOR INDEPENDENCE 1944–1948
Documents from official and private sources
HMSO 1983–1984 2 volumes illustrated maps
Vol 1 From military occupation to civil government January 1,
1944 to August 31, 1946 1078 pp
Vol 2 From general strike to independence August 31, 1946
to January 4, 1948 921pp

I 57 UNITED STATES ARMY
A POCKET GUIDE TO BURMA
United States: Special Service Division US Army Pamphlet
Guide for US servicemen

I 58 WINDSOR, Neville
BURMA: LAND OF MY DREAMS
Jasmine Publications 1996 105pp SC
The impact of war on an Euro-Asian family

37

Section J
The Gurkhas

Books listed here are exclusively concerned with Gurkha regiments. References to Gurkhas are found in many other sections.

J1   BICKERSTETH, Anthony Charles
ODTAA being extracts from the diary of an officer who served with the 4/10TH Gurkha Rifles in Manipur and Burma
Aberdeen University Press: Privately printed 1953 258pp
port maps
20 Indian Division

J2   BISHOP, Edward
BETTER TO DIE: the story of the Gurkhas
New English Library 1976 157pp illustrated maps

J3   FARWELL, Byron
THE GURKHAS
New York: W W Norton 1990 317pp illustrated map sc

J4   *GIBBS, H R K
HISTORICAL RECORDS OF THE SIXTH GURKHA RIFLES Vol II
1919–1948
Gale & Polden 1955

J5   GILMORE, Scott
A CONNECTICUT YANKEE IN THE 8TH GURKHA RIFLES: a Burma memoir
Washington: Brassey's 1995 301pp illustrated

J6   *GUPTA, S C
THE STORY OF GURKHA VCs
Gurkha Museum 1993

J7   *GYI, M
GORKHALI AYO: Gurkha soldiers in the battle for Imphal as told to Marty Kufus (*Command* May 16 – June 1992)

J8   JAMES, Harold and SHEIL-SMALL
      THE GURKHAS
      Stackpole 1965 291pp illustrated map

J9   LEATHART, Scott
      WITH THE GURKHAS: India, Burma, Singapore, Malaya,
      Indonesia 1940–1959
      Pentland Press 1996 270pp illustrated
      With 3rd/9th Gurkha Rifles in 77th Brigade (Chindits)

J10   LUNT, James
      JAI SIXTH! The story of the 6th Q E O Gurkha Rifles
      1817–1994
      Leo Cooper 1994 239 pp illustrated maps
      Battalions served in 19th Indian Division and with the
      Chindits

J11   PALSOKAR, R D
      HISTORY OF THE 5TH GORKHA RIFLES (FRONTIER FORCE)
      Vol III 1858–1991
      Shillong: the regiment 1991 317pp illustrated maps
      Chapter 10 covers the campaign in Burma

J12   PALSOKAR, R D
      RED POMPONS: History of the 8th Gorkha Rifles
      Privately Published 1993

J13   SHEIL-SMALL, Denis
      GREEN SHADOWS: a Gurkha story
      Kimber 1982 198pp illustrated map

J14   *STEVENS, G R
      HISTORY OF THE 2ND K E O GURKHA RIFLES, THE SIRMOOR
      RIFLES Vol III 1921–1948
      Gale & Polden 1952

J15   *STEVENS, G R
      THE 9TH GURKHA RIFLES Vol II 1937–1947
      Butler & Tanner 1953

Section K

Unit and Formation Histories

Regimental histories have been included in the Library if battalions of the regiments played a substantial part in the Burma Campaign. Other histories cover divisions or special branches of the service.

K1 AGGETT, W J P
THE BLOODY ELEVENTH: history of the Devonshire Regiment
Vol III 1915–1969
Exeter: *The Regiment* 1995 704pp illustrated maps
Burma Campaign Chapter 20

K2 *ANONYMOUS
HISTORY OF 17TH INDIAN DIVISION July 1941 – December
1945
Calcutta 1946

K3 *ANONYMOUS
THE BLACK CAT DIVISION: 17th Indian Division
New Delhi 1946

K4 ANONYMOUS – (SPOTTISWOODE)
DAGGER DIVISION: story of the 19th Indian Division
Bombay: Government of India War Department n.d. 50pp
illustrated map
(photocopy)

K5 ANONYMOUS
A HAPPY FAMILY: the story of the 20th Indian Division April
1942 – August 1945
New Delhi: Director of Public Relations GHQ n.d. 52pp
illustrated maps SC

K6 *ANONYMOUS
THE 23RD INDIAN DIVISION
Government of India War Department

K7 *ANONYMOUS
THE FIGHTING FIFTH: history of the Fifth Indian Division
Government of India: War Dept

K8 *ANONYMOUS
TIGER HEAD: the story of the 26th Indian Division
Government of India War Department

K9 ANONYMOUS
THE HISTORY OF THE 1ST BATTALION THE LINCOLNSHIRE
REGIMENT IN INDIA, ARAKAN, BURMA AND SUMATRA:
September 1939 to October 1946
The Regiment 1949 75pp illustrated maps SC
In 26th Indian Division

K10 ANONYMOUS
OPERATIONS OF THE 1ST AND 2ND BATTALIONS THE QUEEN'S
ROYAL REGIMENT IN BURMA DURING WORLD WAR II
The Queen's Royal Surrey Regiment Museum 2nd ed 1991
42pp illustrated maps SC
7th Indian Division and Chindits

K11 ANONYMOUS
KING GEORGE V'S OWN BENGAL SAPPERS AND MINERS
OFFICERS ASSOCIATION: Unit Record 1939–1947
The Association 120pp
Lists of units, officers, awards, etc

K12 *ANONYMOUS
NORTH RHODESIA REGIMENT, 3RD BATTALION BURMA
1945–1946
Lusaka: Government printer 1946

K13 ANONYMOUS
THE ROYAL WEST AFRICAN FRONTIER FORCE: Farewell
Tattoo Arakan 19th September 1946
Unpublished pamphlet

K14 ANONYMOUS
MEET THE WEST AFRICAN SOLDIER
West Africa: General Headquarters n.d. 22pp (photocopy)
A brief introduction for members of HM's Forces about to
serve in British West Africa

K15 BAKER, Richard
BURMA POST: a personal story of airmails and other activities in the Burma campaign 1944–1945
Churchman Publishing 1989 160pp map SC
Army postal services 4 Corps

K16 BELL, A C
HISTORY OF THE MANCHESTER REGIMENT, 1ST AND 2ND BATTALIONS 1922–1948
Sherratt 1954 574pp illustrated maps
Chapters 8 and 9 refer to Burma Campaign

K17 *BETHAM Geoffrey and GEARY
THE GOLDEN GALLEY: the story of the Second Punjab Regiment 1761–1947
1956 343pp illustrated maps

K18 BIRDWOOD, Lord
THE WORCESTERSHIRE REGIMENT 1922–1950
Gale & Polden 1952 317pp illustrated maps
7th Battalion in 2nd British Division

K19 BRELSFORD, W V
THE STORY OF THE NORTHERN RHODESIA REGIMENT
Galago Publishing 1990 134pp illustrated

K20 BURNETT, F T
KEEPING UP WITH THE HUNT: 268th Indian Infantry Brigade
Privately published [1983?]
An independent brigade of XIVth Army

K21 BRETT-JAMES, Anthony
BALL OF FIRE: the 5th Indian Division in the Second World War
Gale & Polden 1951 495pp illustrated maps

K22 CAREW, Tim
THE ROYAL NORFOLK REGIMENT (The 9th Regiment of Foot)
Hamish Hamilton 1967 157pp illustrated
In 2nd British Division

K23 CHAPLIN, J B
ACTION IN BURMA 1942–1945
London 1984 230pp illustrated maps
21st Mountain Regt RA in 17th Indian Division

K24 CLABBY, J
THE HISTORY OF THE ROYAL ARMY VETERINARY CORPS
1919–1961
J A Allen 1963 244pp illustrated maps
Chapters 6 and 7 cover India and Burma

K25 CLAYTON, Anthony
FOREARMED: A HISTORY OF THE INTELLIGENCE CORPS
Brassey's (UK) 1993 illustrated
References to Burma in Chapter 10

K26 CONNOLLY, Malcolm L
3RD CARABINIERS (PRINCE OF WALES'S) DRAGOON GUARDS
Second World War 1939–1945
Privately published 37pp illustrated SC
254th Armoured Brigade – Imphal, Mandalay, Irrawaddy

K27 CONNORS, B P
A SHORT ILLUSTRATED HISTORY OF THE SECOND DIVISION
1809–1965
HQ 2 Div 1965 40pp illustrated SC

K28 DAS, Chand N
THE RAJPUTANA RIFLES: BRIEF HISTORY
New Delhi: Reliance Publishing 1995 154pp illustrated
maps

K29 DAVIES, E H C
64TH INDIAN INFANTRY BRIGADE WAR HISTORY 1942–1946
Privately printed 1997 145pp ports maps SC
In 19th Indian Division

K30 DOULTON, A J F
THE FIGHTING COCK: being the history of the 23rd Indian
Division 1942–1947
Gale & Polden 1951

K31 *DUNCAN, W E and others
THE ROYAL ARTILLERY COMMEMORATIVE BOOK 1939–1945
Bell 1950 781pp illustrated maps

K32 *ENRIQUES, C M
THE STORY OF THE BURMA RIFLES

K33 FOSTER, Geoffry
36TH DIVISION: NORTH BURMA 1944–1945
Edson 1946 64pp illustrated maps

K34 *GLOVER, Michael
HISTORY OF THE ROYAL WELCH FUSILIERS
Leo Cooper 1989

K35 GODDEN, Rumer
BENGAL JOURNEY: a story of the part played by women in the
province 1939–1945
Calcutta: Longmans 1945 136pp illustrated
Sponsored by WVS (Bengal)

K36 GRAHAM, C A L
THE HISTORY OF THE INDIAN MOUNTAIN ARTILLERY
Gale & Polden 1957 485pp illustrated maps

K37 GROUNDS, Tom
SOME LETTERS FROM BURMA: the story of the 25th Dragoons
at war
Parapress Ltd 1994 284pp illustrated maps

K38 *HALLAM
HISTORY OF LANCASHIRE FUSILIERS
Sutton 1993

K39 HANLEY, Gerald
MONSOON VICTORY
Collins 1946 256pp illustrated
11th (East African) Division in the Kabaw Valley 1944

K40 HART, Peter
AT THE SHARP END: from Le Paradis to Kohima 2nd Bn the
Royal Norfolk Regiment
Leo Cooper: Pen & Sword Books 1998 224pp illustrated maps

K41 HAVERS, Norman
MARCH ON! An infantry battalion in England,
India and Burma
Square One 1992 284pp illustrated maps
2nd Bn the Dorsetshire Regiment in 2nd Division

K42 *HAYWOOD, A H W and CLARKE
THE HISTORY OF THE ROYAL WEST AFRICAN
FRONTIER FORCE
Gale & Polden 1964 555pp illustrated maps
81st and 82nd (West African) Divisions served in
Burma 1943–1945

K43 HILL, John
CHINA DRAGONS: A RIFLE COMPANY AT WAR
Blandford 1991 192pp illustrated maps
2nd Bn Royal Berkshires 1944–1945

K44 *HOMER, Harry
NO TIGERS IN THE JUNGLE
Published by the author
The RAF Regiment in Burma

K45 JOHNSON, E (compiler)
A BRIEF HISTORY OF THE MACHINE GUN BATTALION,
THE JAT REGIMENT 1941–1946
Bangalore: Higginbothams 1947 86pp illustrated maps

K46 KARIM, Afsir
THE STORY OF THE INDIAN AIRBORNE TROOPS
New Delhi: Lancer International 1993 394pp maps

K47 LANE, Arthur
THANBAZAYAT: REGISTER OF GRAVES (3771)
No publication details or pagination. Lane 1995
The Thanbazayat war cemetery is forty miles from
Moulmein

K48 MacFETRIDGE, Charles H T and WARREN
TALES OF THE MOUNTAIN GUNNERS
Blackwood 1974 346pp illustrated maps

K49 MACKENZIE, Tony
44 COMMANDO: ACHNACARRY TO THE ARAKAN: a diary of
the commando at war, August 1943 to March 1947
Tom Donovan 1996 170pp illustrated maps

K50 McCLEOD D
HISTORY OF THE 130TH FIELD REGIMENT AND ITS BURMA
CAMPAIGNS
The author 1996 216pp maps SC

K51 MUIR, Augustus
THE FIRST OF FOOT: the history of the Royal Scots (The
Royal Regiment)
R S History Committee 1961 520pp illustrated maps
In 14th Indian Division and 2nd Division: Arakan,
Assam/Manipur

K52 NEILD, Eric
WITH PEGASUS IN INDIA: the story of 153 Gurkha Parachute
Battalion
Nashville: the Battery Press n.d. 110pp illustrated maps

K53 OBA, Sadao
THE 'JAPANESE' WAR: London University's WWII secret
teaching programme and the experts sent to help to beat
Japan; translated by Anne Kaneko
The Japan Library 1995 179pp illustrated maps

K54 PAGE, Malcolm
A HISTORY OF THE KING'S AFRICAN RIFLES AND EAST
AFRICAN FORCES
Leo Cooper 1998 317pp illustrated maps
11th East African Division, 22nd and 28th E A Brigades in
Burma (Chapter 8)

K55 PALIT, D K
SENTINALS OF THE NORTH-EAST
New Delhi: Palit & Palit 333pp illustrated maps

K56 PERKINS, Roger (compiler)
REGIMENTS: regiments and corps of the British Empire and
Commonwealth 1758–1993: a critical bibliography of their
published histories
The author 1994 806pp

K57 PERRETT, Bryan
TANK TRACKS TO RANGOON: the story of British armour in
Burma
Robert Hale 1992 255pp illustrated maps SC
First published in 1978

K58 RISSIK, David
THE DLI AT WAR: the history of the Durham Light Infantry
1939–1945
DLI 1952 368pp illustrated maps
With 14th Indian Division in Arakan and 2nd British
Division Assam/Manipur

K59 ROBERTS, Michael R
GOLDEN ARROW: the story of the 7th Indian Division in the
Second World War 1939–1945
Gale & Polden 1952 326pp illustrated maps

K60 ROBERTSON, G W
THE ROSE AND THE ARROW ...136th (1st West Lancashire)
Field Regt RA 1939–1946
136th Field Regt Old Comrades Ass 1986 338pp illustrated
maps SC
In 7th Indian Division

K61 SANDES, E W C
FROM PYRAMID TO PAGODA: the story of the West Yorkshire
Regiment (The Prince of Wales's Own) in the war 1939–1945
and afterwards
1951 306pp ports maps
1st and 2nd Battalions served in Burma

K62 SHIRREFF, David
BURMA STORY
Unpublished n.d. 32pp typescript
5th King's African Rifles Kabaw Valley and Chindwin
September – December 1944

K63 *STEYN, Peter
THE HISTORY OF THE ASSAM REGIMENT Vol I 1941–1947
Calcutta: Orient Longmans 1959

K64 *SUGDEN, J P
BURMA CAMPAIGN: artillery of 19th (Indian) [Dagger]
Division
The author

K65 *TAYLOR, Jeremy
THE DEVONS
White Swan Press

K66 *TURNBULL, Patrick
HISTORY OF THE TWELFTH ARMY from its formation on May
28, 1945 to the end of operations September 1945

K67 *VERMA, S and ANAND
THE CORPS OF INDIAN ENGINEERS 1939–1947
Government of India Ministry of Defence Historical Section
1974

K68 WAIT, Rex
MY BURMA CAMPAIGN
Unpublished typescript 1998 6pp
18th Field Regt (SP) Royal Artillery

K69 WHITE, O G W
STRAIGHT ON FOR TOKYO: the war history of the 2nd Bn the
Dorsetshire Regiment (54th Foot)
Gale & Polden 1948 444pp illustrated maps
In 2nd British Division Assam/Manipur

K70 *WHITE, Steve
MORE WARTIME MEMOIRS
Privately printed
99th Field Regt RA in 2nd British Division

K71 *WOMEN'S AUXILIARY SERVICE (Burma)
THE WASBIES: the story of the Women's Auxiliary Service
(Burma)
War Facts Press [1946] 80pp illustrated maps
Written by K. Vellacott Jones, 2nd Lt WAS(B) 1945–6
contains complete list of all members, 1942–1946

Section L
Autobiographies, Biographies and Diaries

L1 BUCHAN, Alastair and VILLIERS
TWENTY-FIVE YEARS 1919 -1944: Major Alastair Guy Spens
Campbell MC FRGS
Alcuin Press 1950 99pp port map

L2 CALVERT, Michael
SLIM
Ballantine Books 1973 160pp illustrated maps SC
General Slim commanded XIV Army

L3 COLLINS, R J
LORD WAVELL (1883–1941): a military biography
Hodder & Stoughton 1948 488pp illustrated maps

L4 CONNELL, John
WAVELL SUPREME COMMANDER 1941–1943
Collins 1969 317pp illustrated maps
His tenure as Commander (American, British, Dutch,
Australian area)

L5 EVANS, Geoffrey
SLIM AS MILITARY COMMANDER
Batsford 1969 239pp illustrated maps

L6 EVANS, Humphreys
THIMAYYA OF INDIA: a soldier's life
New York: Harcourt Brace 1960 307pp illustrated

L7 FERGUSSON, Bernard
THE TRUMPET IN THE HALL 1930–1958
Collins 1970 maps
His military autobiography by a Chindit Brigade
Commander

L8 *HAWLEY, Dennis
THE DEATH OF WINGATE
Merlin Books 1994 340pp illustrated

L9 HAY, Alice
THERE WAS A MAN OF GENIUS, letters to my grandson, Orde
Jonathan Wingate
Spearman 1963 158pp illustrated
Wingate was the author's son-in-law

L10 HOUGH, Richard
MOUNTBATTEN: HERO OF OUR TIME
Weidenfeld 1980 302pp illustrated

L11 LEWIN, Ronald
SLIM THE STANDARD BEARER: a biography of Field-Marshal
The Viscount Slim
Leo Cooper 1976 365pp illustrated maps

L12 MAULE, Henry
SPEARHEAD GENERAL: the epic story of General Sir Frank
Messervy and his men in Eritrea, North Africa and Burma
Odhams Press 1961 384pp illustrated maps
Messervy commanded 7th Indian Division

L13 MEAD, Peter
ORDE WINGATE AND THE HISTORIANS
Merlin Books 206pp illustrated maps SC

L14 MOSLEY, Leonard
GIDEON GOES TO WAR
New York: Scribners 1955 256pp illustrated
Life and campaigns of Wingate

L15 *MOUNTBATTEN, Louis the Earl Mountbatten of Burma
PERSONAL DIARY SACSEA 1943–1946 ed by Philip Ziegler
Collins 1988 371pp illustrated maps

L16 *MURPHY, Ray
THE LAST VICEROY: the life and times of Rear Admiral the
Earl Mountbatten of Burma
Jarrolds 1948 270pp illustrated

L17 NEWHALL, Sue Mayes
THE DEVIL IN GOD'S OLD MAN
New York: W W Norton 1969 253pp
Biography of the Burma Surgeon Gordon Seagrave

L18 PALIT, D K
MAJOR GENERAL A A RUDRA: his service in three armies and
two World Wars
New Delhi: Reliance Publishing 1997 364pp illustrated
Rudra 1896-1993 one of the first Indians to be granted a
King's Commission. From 1943 he served on the staff at
GHQ dealing with the INA and other matters

L19 POCOCK, Tom
FIGHTING GENERAL: the public and private campaigns of
General Sir Walter Walker
Collins 1973 280pp illustrated maps
Walter Walker commanded 4/8th Gurkhas in 7th Indian
Division

L20 POWNALL, Sir Henry
CHIEF OF STAFF: the diaries of Lieutenant-General Sir Henry
Pownall; edited by Brian Bond
Leo Cooper
Vol 1 1933-1940 431pp illustrated
Vol 2 1940-1944 234pp illustrated
Chief of Staff to Wavell and Mountbatten

L21 ROONEY, David
MAD MIKE: A LIFE OF MICHAEL CALVERT
Leo Cooper 1997 219pp illustrated maps
The guerrilla expert and Chindit Brigadier

L22 ROONEY, David
STILWELL
Pan/Ballantine 160pp illustrated maps SC

L23 ROONEY, David
WINGATE AND THE CHINDITS: redressing the balance
Arms & Armour Press 1994 256pp illustrated maps

L24 ROYLE, Trevor
ORDE WINGATE: IRREGULAR SOLDIER
Weidenfield & Nicolson 1995 367pp illustrated

L25 SWINSON, Arthur
FOUR SAMURAI: a quartet of Japanese army commanders in
the Second World War

Hutchinson 1968 262pp illustrated maps
Homma; Yamashita; Mutaguchi; Honda

L26 SYKES, Christopher
ORDE WINGATE
Collins 1959 575pp illustrated maps
Cleveland Ohio: World Publishing 1959 575pp illustrated
maps

L27 TUCHMAN, Barbara W
STILWELL AND THE AMERICAN EXPERIENCE IN CHINA
1911–1945
New York: Macmillan 1977 636pp illustrated maps

L28 TULLOCH, Derek
WINGATE IN PEACE AND WAR; edited by Arthur Swinson
Macdonald 1972 300pp port

L29 WAVELL, Archibald, Field-Marshal the Viscount
WAVELL THE VICEROY'S JOURNAL; edited by Penderel Moon
Oxford University Press 1973 528pp illustrated map

L30 *WILKES, Lyall
FESTING-FIELD MARSHAL
Book Guild 1991

L31 WILLIAMS, Gron
THE FRANK OWEN STORY
Square One 1993 175pp

L32 WILLIAMS, J H
ELEPHANT BILL
Hart Davis 1950 320pp illustrated maps
Penguin Books
'OC Elephants' XIVth Army

L33 ZIEGLER, Philip
MOUNTBATTEN
Collins 1985

Section M
Personal Narratives

The books in this section are personal accounts of combat
experience. They cover every phase of the Campaign. Some
of these memoirs begin with service in the UK and include
accounts of travel in Africa and India on the way to Burma.

M1 *ADAMSON, Arthur
AN ARTILLERY OP IN BURMA
The author 1994
With 7th Indian Division

M2 ALLAN, James R
PERSONAL PAPERS
Notes on Allied Orders of Battle, the Japanese Armed Forces
etc etc

M3 ALLAN, James R
IN THE TRADE OF WAR
Parapress Ltd 1994 194pp illustrated
With the Green Howards in Arakan

M4 ANONYMOUS
JAPANESE NEWSPAPER ACCOUNTS OF 1990 VISIT TO JAPAN BY
BRITISH VETERANS

M5 ARMSTRONG, Geoffrey
THE SPARKS FLY UPWARDS: an experience
Gooday 1991 236pp illustrated maps
136th Field Regt RA – Arakan 1943 to victory in 7th Indian
Division

M6 ARNOLD, Ralph
A VERY QUIET WAR
Hart-Davis 1962 176pp
Deputy Director of Public Relations SEAC

M7 BEATON, Cecil
FAR EAST
Batsford 1945 111pp illustrated

Diary of a journey to Asia during the war with one chapter on Assam and Burma

M8 BOULTON, Norman
TAFFY'S WAR
Minerva Press 1997 69pp SC
Author served in Royal Artillery and Royal Signals

M9 BRADLEY, James
TOWARDS THE SETTING SUN: an escape from the Thailand-Burma railway 1943
Wellington NSW: J M Fuller 1984 158pp illustrated maps

M10 BRETT-JAMES, Anthony
REPORT MY SIGNALS
Hennel Locke 1948 360pp illustrated maps
A Signals Officer in 5th Indian Division

M11 BRISTOW, R C B
MEMORIES OF THE BRITISH RAJ: a soldier in India
Johnson 1974 208pp illustrated map
Chapter 5 covers Burma

M12 CAREW, Tim
ALL THIS AND A MEDAL TOO
Constable 1954 261pp
Service in Royal Horse Guards, the Parachute Regiment and in Burma with Gurkhas

M13 CHAPMAN, G P
THE LAMPI: a story about some gunners
Calcutta: Thacker Spink 1944 86pp illustrated maps
Road building from Lakhipur to Bishenpur

M14 *CLARK, M
HIGH ENDEAVOURS: Miles and Beryl I Smeeton
Grafton 1991

M15 CLARKE, A E
RETURN TO SINGAPORE
Newton 1995 46pp illustrated map SC
2nd Bn West Yorkshire Regt

M16 CLARKE, Fred
THE ROAD TO SPIDERPORE
Rocket Publishing 1995 172pp

M17 CLIFFORD, Francis
DESPERATE JOURNEY
Hodder 1979 192pp
Escape from Burma into China 1942

M18 CLIFFORD, J Francis
THE HILLS OF BISHENPUR AND THE ADVANCE INTO
CENTRAL BURMA
Unpublished n.d. 15pp typescript
Author was in Northamptonshire Regiment

M19 *COLLISTER, Peter
THEN A SOLDIER
Churchman 1985
From retreat to victory

M20 COOPER, K W
THE LITTLE MEN
Hale 1992 186pp illustrated map SC
A platoon of 2nd Bn the Border Regiment

M21 COOPER, Raymond
'B' COMPANY, 9TH BATTALION THE BORDER REGIMENT: one
man's war in Burma 1942–1944
Dobson 1978 152pp illustrated maps
17th Indian Division

M22 COOPER, William J
DESERT SAND TO JUNGLE TRAIL: one man's war 1940-1946
Bookmarque 1997 192pp SC
A soldier in the Queen's, 16th Brigade

M23 *COULTHARD, G
FROM PRIVATE TO TROOPER, BACK TO PRIVATE
Pentland 1994

M24 *CROSBY, M G M
IRREGULAR SOLDIER
XB Publications 1993 262pp

M25 DAVIS, Patrick
A CHILD AT ARMS
Hutchinson 1970 258pp maps
In 4/8th Gurkha Rifles

M26 DURNFORD-SLATER, John
BRANCH LINE TO BURMA
Macdonald 1958

M27 EVANS, Geoffrey
THE DESERT AND THE JUNGLE
Kimber 1959 206pp illustrated maps
This account of five battles includes the Admin Box, Arakan
February 1944 and crossing of the Irrawaddy at Nyaungu
January – February 1945

M28 FORTEATH, G M
PIPES, KUKRIS AND NIPS
Pentland Press 1991 149pp

M29 FRASER, George Macdonald
QUARTERED SAFE OUT HERE: a recollection of the war in
Burma
Harvill 1992 247pp
9th Bn The Border Regiment in 17th Indian Division

M30 GADSDON, Peter H
AN AMATEUR AT WAR
Privately published 90pp SC illustrated maps
The author served in 4/14th Punjab Regt 7th Indian Division

M31 GORDINE, E T C
A PATRIOT'S BOAST
Stockwell 1975 210 pp

M32 *GORDON, Oliver L
FIGHT IT OUT
Kimber 1957 238pp illustrated

M33 GRANT, Peter
A HIGHLANDER GOES TO WAR: a memoir 1939–1946
Pentland Press 1995 147pp
Author served in Q O Cameron Highlanders

M34 HAMMOND, B A T
REFLECTIONS ON A WAR DIARY
Edited version of War Diary of 16th Field Regt Royal
Artillery 2nd British Division India and Burma 1942–1945

M35 HAYTER, Adrian
THE SECOND STEP
Hodder & Stoughton 1962 223pp illustrated
Experiences in the Indian Army

M36 HEDLEY, John
JUNGLE FIGHTER, CHINDIT & SOE AGENT IN BURMA
1941–1945
Tom Donovan 1996 148pp maps
The retreat, the second Chindit operation, Force 136

M37 HENSLOW, John
A SAPPER IN THE FORGOTTEN ARMY
The author 1986 261pp illustrated maps
With 23rd Indian Division

M38 HISCOX, Norman G
UNDER TWO FLAGS
Pentland Press 1997 138pp illustrated maps
A signaller in a Field Regt from Tamu to Rangoon

M39 *HOWARTH Patrick
SPECIAL OPERATIONS
Routledge 1955
pp 210–23 The Great Elephant Trek by J H Williams

M40 HUMPHREYS, Roy
TO STOP A RISING SUN: reminiscences of war time in India
and Burma
Alan Sutton 1996 214pp
Contributions by numerous ex-service personnel

M41 HUNT, Gordon
ONE MORE RIVER
Collins 1965 255pp illustrated maps
Bhamo to China 1942

M42 *JACK, Ian M
A SOLDIER'S TALE
Stanley Castle 1995 44pp map
Author served in 6/9th Jat Regiment

M43 *JONES, C B
NOT FORGETTING THE ELEPHANTS
Book Guild 1983

M44 JONES, W H
A SOLDIER REMINISCES
Privately published n.d. 39pp
Service in 1st Bn Royal Welch Fusiliers

M45 JOWERS, John Edward
GETTING MY KNEES BROWN: the war diary ...
January 1, 1943 – April 28, 1946
Privately published 1997 185pp illustrated map SC
Service in 6th Indian Air Formation Signals

M46 *LOWRY, M A
AN INFANTRY COMPANY IN ARAKAN AND KOHIMA
Gale & Polden 1950 146pp

M47 LYDALL, Edward
ENOUGH OF ACTION
Book Guild 252pp

M48 MacFETRIDGE, Charles H T
HOW THE MILITARY CAME TO DIGBOI, UPPER ASSAM IN 1941
Unpublished 1998 6pp typescript
AA Defence of oil installations

M49 MACKENZIE, Compton
ALL OVER THE PLACE
Chatto & Windus 1949 292pp
The author's diary of journeys made while writing Eastern Epic

M50 MACKENZIE, K P
OPERATION RANGOON JAIL
Christopher Johnson 1954 201pp illustrated
Colonel MacKenzie was taken prisoner at Sittang,
February 22, 1942

M51 MACKAY, R R
THE LAST OF THE DOZEN
Pentland Press 1996 184pp map
A soldier in the Royal Engineers

M52 McCLINTOCK, J Dewar
THE MANIPUR ROAD
Brown, Watson n.d. 159pp SC

M53 MAGENER, Rolf
PRISONER'S BLUFF
Hart-Davis 1954 239pp ports map
Two German POWs escape from India and join the
Japanese forces in Arakan

M54 MASTERS, John
BUGLES AND A TIGER: a personal adventure
The Reprint Society 1957 (first published by
Michael Joseph 1956) 319pp
Pre-1939 service in 2/4th POWs Gurkha Rifles

M55 MASTERS, John
THE ROAD PAST MANDALAY: a personal narrative
New York: Harper 1961 341pp illustrated
Service with Gurkhas and Chindits

M56 MAUNG-MAUNG U
TO A SOLDIER SON
Rangoon: U Kya Wohn 1974 158pp

M57 MELLORS, J
SHOTS IN THE DARK
London Magazine Editions 1974 160pp
The author served in a Mountain Regiment RA

M58 *MITCHELL, Harold
AGAINST THE ODDS
The Book Guild 1990
6/15th Punjab Regt from Meiktila to victory

M59 MUNN, A W
A FRAGMENT OF LIFE: THE BURMA EPISODE
Avon Books 1996 253pp illustrated map
A tribute to the British infantrymen who fought in Burma

M60 NUNNELEY, John
TALES FROM THE KING'S AFRICAN RIFLES: a last flourish of empire
Askari Books 1998 221pp illustrated maps
11th (East African) Division in the Kabaw Valley

M61 OATTS, L Balfour
THE JUNGLE IN ARMS
Kimber 1962 207pp map

M62 PARKINSON, J D and HORNBY
ALONG O MY OLD GREY MULE
Holden Publications 1996 68pp illustrated maps SC
RAVC officers on the care of mules in XIV Army

M63 *PEACOCK, Geraldine
THE LIFE OF A JUNGLE WALLA: reminiscences in the life
of Lt Col E H Peacock DSO MC
Stockwell 1958 134pp illustrated

M64 *PICKFORD, S C S
DESTINATION RANGOON
Gee & Son 1989 296pp

M65 *POTTER, J D
NO TIME FOR BREAKFAST: MEMOIRS
Melrose 1951 240pp illustrated

M66 PRENDERGAST, John
PRENDER'S PROGRESS: A SOLDIER IN INDIA 1931-1947
Cassell 1979 256pp illustrated
1/5th Punjabis in Arakan and 19th Indian Divisions

M67 RODGER, George
RED MOON RISING
Cresset press 1943 127pp illustrated
By a war correspondent for *Life*

M68 *ROSE, D
OFF THE RECORD: the life and letters of a
Black Watch Officer
Spellmount 1996

M69 SCHLAEFLI, Robin
EMERGENCY SAHIB (of Queen's, Sikhs and Dagger Division)
Leach 1992 159pp illustrated maps
The Dagger Division was 19th Indian Division

M70 *SHARP, Robin
THE LIFE OF AN ECO IN INDIA
Pentland 1994

M71 SHIPSTER, John
WHEN THE MIST WAS ON THE RICE FIELDS
Unpublished 199- 132pp illustrated maps
7/2nd Punjab Regt in 7th Indian Division

M72 SHORT, Stanley W
ON BURMA'S EASTERN FRONTIER
Marshall, Morgan & Scott 1945 144pp illustrated
A missionary's story

M73 SLIM, William Field Marshal the Viscount
UNOFFICIAL HISTORY 1959
Cassell 251pp maps
'Little battles and unimportant Skirmishes' – the author

M74 SMEETON, Miles
A CHANGE OF JUNGLES
Hart-Davis 1962 192pp
Author commanded an Armoured Regiment

M75 *SMEETON, Miles
A TASTE OF THE HILLS
Hart-Davis 1961 207pp illustrated

M76 SMITH, H C
HOSTILITIES ONLY: tales of an amateur soldier in
World War II
Privately published n.d. unpaged maps
In 4th Bn Royal West Kents

M77 STREET, Robert
A BRUMMIE IN BURMA
Barny Books 100pp illustrated maps SC
Author served in 4th Bn Royal West Kents at Kohima

M78 *SWEET-ESCOTT, Bickham
BAKER STREET IRREGULAR
Methuen 1965 278pp

M79 TEWARI, K K
A SOLDIER'S VOYAGE OF SELF-DISCOVERY
Auroville n.d. 182pp illustrated maps SC

M80 TRENCH, C C
THE INDIAN ARMY AND THE KING'S ENEMIES
312pp illustrated
One or two chapters on Burma

M81 TURNER, A S
AN ENGINEER IN THE WAR: bomb disposal, jungle, Sikhs
Onyx Publishing 1998 104pp illustrated SC
Sikh Engineer Battalion in XIVth Army

M82 UNIACKE, Richard John
DIARY 16TH FIELD REGT ROYAL ARTILLERY INDIA & BURMA
June 1942 – November 1945
Typescript unpublished:
Version 1 annotations by B A T Hammond
Version 2 with marginal notes by D H Woodcock

Section N
Medical Services

N1 *UNITED STATES DEPARTMENT OF THE ARMY
ORIGINAL REPORTS ON MILITARY MEDICINE IN INDIA AND
BURMA DURING SECOND WORLD WAR 1969

N2 ASHFORD-BROWN, William Hay
COLD HANDS: being the memoirs of a Scottish G P
Avon Books 107pp illustrated

N3 BATY, John A
SURGEON IN THE JUNGLE WAR
Kimber 1979 196pp illustrated

N4 BEAUMONT, Winifred
A DETAIL ON THE BURMA FRONT
BBC 1977 160pp map
An Army nurse

N5 BOLTON, Angela
THE MATURING SUN: an army nurse in India, 1942–1945
Imperial War Museum 1986 218pp illustrated maps

N6 CREW, F A E
HISTORY OF THE SECOND WORLD WAR – MEDICAL
SERVICES
HMSO 1966 800pp
The Army Medical Services: Vol V Burma

N7 EVANS, Sir Charles
A DOCTOR IN XIVTH ARMY: BURMA 1944–1945
Leo Cooper 1998 198pp illustrated maps
Experiences in a Malaria Forward Treatment Unit and as
Regimental Medical officer in 20th Indian Division

N8 MAURICE, Dick
FROM CRADLE TO WAR: my first three decades 1915–1945
The Book Guild 193pp maps
A doctor in XIV Army

N9 HAMMOND, C V
PACK UP YOUR MEDICINES 1939–1947: an account of the
work of pharmacists in the services during the Second
World War
Purnvic Press 1998 414pp illustrated

N10 PRASAD, B
OFFICIAL HISTORY OF THE INDIAN ARMED FORCES IN THE
SECOND WORLD WAR 1939–45 – Medical Services
Medicine, Surgery and Pathology
Combined Inter-Services Historical Section India & Pakistan
1955 906pp illustrated

N11 PRASAD, B
OFFICIAL HISTORY OF THE INDIAN ARMED FORCES IN THE
SECOND WORLD WAR 1939–45 – Medical Services
Administration
Combined Inter Services Historical Section India & Pakistan
1953 679pp illustrated

N12 *RAINA, B L
WORLD WAR II MEDICAL SERVICES: INDIA Commonwealth
1990

N13 ROBERTSON, Marian
SISTER SAHIBS: the VADs with 14th Army 1944–1946
The Book Guild 1988 168pp
A British nurse's experiences 1944/45

N14 RODRIGUEZ, Helen
HELEN OF BURMA
Collins 1983 187pp illustrated
A hospital matron in pre-war and Japanese occupied Burma

N15 SEAGRAVE, Gordon S
BURMA SURGEON
W W Norton 1943 295pp illustrated

N16 *SEAGRAVE, Gordon
THE LIFE OF A BURMA SURGEON
1960 SC

N17 SEAGRAVE, Gordon
BURMA SURGEON RETURNS
W W Norton 1946 268pp illustrated maps

N18 *STONE, J E
THE UNITED STATES ARMY MEDICAL SERVICE IN COMBAT IN
INDIA AND BURMA 1942–1945
Ann Arbor: Michigan University Microfilm International
1986

N19 WILLSON, Leslie
A SON OF THE RAJ
Pentland Press 1996 184pp illustrated maps
The author served as a Medical Officer in 2 Division

Section O

The Indian National Army

Most of the literature about the INA originates in India. This section also includes biographies of Subhas Chandra Bose.

01 ANONYMOUS
A FORGOTTEN ARMY
New Delhi: National Committee for celebration of Golden Jubilee of Provisional Government of Azad Hind 1993–1994 56pp illustrated map SC

02 ARSHAD, Raja Muhammad
THE RETREAT
Written in the Red Fort, Delhi October 1945 n.d.

03 BAKSHI, Akhil
THE ROAD TO FREEDOM: travels through Singapore, Malaysia, Burma and India in the footsteps of the Indian National Army
New Delhi: Odyssey Books 1998 114pp illustrated maps

04 BHARGAVA, Moti Lal and GILL
INDIAN NATIONAL ARMY: SECRET SERVICE
New Delhi: Reliance Publishing 1988 136pp ports

05 BHARGAVA, Moti Lal
INDIAN NATIONAL ARMY: TOKYO CADETS
New Delhi: Reliance Publishing 1986 88pp illustrated

06 BOSE, Romen
A WILL FOR FREEDOM
New Delhi: All India INA Committee 1992 50pp

07 CORR, Gerard H
THE WAR OF THE SPRINGING TIGERS
Osprey 1975 200pp port

08 DHILLON, Gurbakhsh Singh
FROM MY BONES: memoirs of the India National Army
(including 1945 Red Fort trial)
New Delhi: Aryan Books 1998 598pp illustrated

09 FAY, Peter Ward
THE FORGOTTEN ARMY: India's armed struggle for
independence
University of Michigan Press 573pp illustrated maps SC

010 *GHOSH, K K
THE INDIA NATIONAL ARMY: Second front of India
independence
Meenakshi Prakashan 1969

011 KHAN, Shahnawaz
MY MEMORIES OF INA AND ITS NETAJI
Delhi: Rajkamal Publications 1946 296pp illustrated

012 KIANI, Mohammad Zaman
INDIA'S FREEDOM STRUGGLE AND THE GREAT INA
New Delhi: Reliance Publishing 1994 268pp illustrated
maps

013 LE BRA, Joyce
JUNGLE ALLIANCE: Japan and the INA
Singapore: Asia Pacific Press 1971

014 MAIKAP, Satish Chandra
NETAJI SUBHAS CHANDRA BOSE AND INDIA WAR OF
INDEPENDENCE
Calcutta: Punashca 1998 374pp illustrated map

015 MAIKAP, Satish Chandra
CHALLENGE TO THE EMPIRE: a study of Netaji (Subhas
Chandra Bose)
New Delhi: Government of India 1993 144pp illustrated SC

016 *MANGAT, G S
INDIAN NATIONAL ARMY: role of India's stuggle for freedom
Gagan 1971

017 MENON, K A K
FROM THE DIARY OF A FREEDOM FIGHTER
Madras: Kavungal Anat 1989 189pp SC

018 PANDIT, H N
THE LAST DAYS OF NETAJI
New Delhi: All India INA Committee 1993 164pp
illustrated map

019 RAO, U Sunder
REMINISCENCES OF AN INA SOLDIER
Mangalore: Sharada Press [1986?] 331pp

020 *ROY, P B
THE GLORY THAT IS INA
Speegura library 1946

021 SARKER, B K
SUBHAS CHANDRA BOSE
(Bengali text)

022 SAREEN, T R
JAPAN AND THE INDIAN NATIONAL ARMY
Delhi: Mounto Publishing House 1996 335pp

023 THIVY, John A & SAFRANI
THE STRUGGLE IN EAST ASIA 1945 66pp
THE MEN FROM IMPHAL by Abid Hasan Safrani 15pp
Calcutta: Netaji Research Bureau 2nd ed 1995 illustrated

024 THE ORACLE: a quarterly review of history, current affairs
and international relations
Calcutta: Netaji Research Bureau
Vol I no 1 Jan 1979; Vol I no 4; Vol II no 2; Vol VI no 1; Vol
VII no 3; Vol VIII no 1; Vol IX no 1; Vol XVI no 4; Vol XVIII
no 1 January, 1996
Vol XVIII no 1 contains complete list of contents 1979–1995.
Contents include documents, speeches and both political and
military articles

025 *TOYE, Hugh
SPRINGING TIGER: a study of a revolutionary
Cassell 1959 258pp illustrated
Subhas Chandra Bose

Section P

Newspapers and Ephemera

P1 *CRUMPLER Hugh
1st Air Commando glides into harm's way
D C Thomson 1962
4pp article from *San Diego Union-Tribune* February 27,
1994 (photocopy)

P2 MOUNTBATTEN, Louis the Earl Mountbatten of Burma
THE STRATEGY OF THE SOUTH-EAST ASIA COMMAND: a
lecture given at the Royal United Service Institution
October 9, 1946
16pp map SC

P3 MISCELLANEOUS NEWSPAPER CLIPPINGS
AND ISSUES 1945
SEAC Souvenir

P4 NORMAN, William
50 YEARS AGO: THE BATTLE OF SITTANG FEBRUARY 16–23,
1942 8pp
WITH THE 2ND BATTALION IN BURMA IN 1942 6pp and 3pp
Articles in *The Iron Duke*: the Regimental journal of the
Duke of Wellington's Regiment. Spring 1992 Winter 1996
Spring 1997

P5 THE SACRIFICE OF CAPTAIN RANDLE
D C Thomson 1962
2pp from *The Victor* no 74
(illustrated boys' weekly comic)

P6 *ROBINSON, D K
Cochran's Air Commandos
8pp article from *Behind the lines* (the journal of US Military
Special Operations) Festus Missouri 1994 illustrated

P7 ROSSETTO, Luigi
THE FIRST AIR COMMANDO
12pp article from *Aerospace Historian* Manhattan, Kansas
1982 (photocopy)

P8 *SEARLE, Ronald
FORTY DRAWINGS
Cambridge University Press 1946

P9 SOUTH-EAST ASIA COMMAND
BURMA: A MIRACLE IN MILITARY ACHIEVEMENT
SEAC [1945] 23pp illustrated maps SC
Written by Frank Owen for the Supreme Allied
Commander

P10 SEAC
LAUGH WITH SEAC n.d.
Calcutta: SACSEA 120pp SC
Cartoons

P11 SMYTH, John
THE LONG RETREAT: the first Burma campaign
Purnell 1967 (Vol 3 part 3 of part-work History of the
Second World War) 12pp illustrated map SC

P12 VEVERS, Denis (compiler)
A COLLECTION of propaganda material, phrase books and
Japanese occupation currency.

P13 VICTORY
VICTORY CARTOONS
Bombay: Thackers Publishers n.d. 70pp
From the *India Command* newspaper

P14 VICTORY IN BURMA: December 1944 – August 1945
Marshall Cavendish 1995 Issue 46 Volume 3 of part-work
Images of War 20pp illustrated map

Section Q

Journals and newsletters

Q1 ANONYMOUS
MOM's Words
Men of the Mohawk Squadrons Association quarterly
newsletter

Q2 BURMA STAR ASSOCIATION
Dekho!
The journal of the Burma Star Association
No 1 1951–
Various formats

Q3 BURMA CAMPAIGN FELLOWSHIP GROUP
Newsletter
No 1 1992–
A5

Q4 425-436 BURMA SQUADRONS ASSOCIATION
Pukka Gen
Newsletter June 1993; March, June, October 1995; March,
July 1996 Canada: Etobicoke, Ontario
A4

Q5 KING, Dwight O
Magazine for former members of US Units in CBI
Theatre October 1996 – January 1999

Q6 FIRST AIR COMMANDO ASSOCIATION
The Basher Blabber
Fall 1993; Winter 1994; 1995 two issues 1996; 1997 S:
Reading, Pennsylvania
A4

Section R
Pictorial Histories

R1 CORPORATION OF LONDON
THEY LIVED TO TELL THE TALE: personal reminiscences of
some of those who served in the Second World War Far
Eastern Campaigns.
The Corporation of London 1995 28pp illustrated map SC

R2 FORTY, George
XIV ARMY AT WAR
Ian Allan 1987 144pp illustrated map

R3 LANE, Arthur
WHEN YOU GO HOME
A Lane Publication 1993 311pp illustrated maps
Lists 22,602 British service men and women who died in
Malaya, Singapore and as prisoners of war

R4 MOSER, Don and others
CHINA-BURMA-INDIA
Alexandria, Virginia: Time-life Books 1978 208pp
illustrated maps

R5 MOUNTBATTEN, Louis the Earl Mountbatten of Burma
MOUNTBATTEN: EIGHTY YEARS IN PICTURES
Book Club Associates 1979 224pp illustrated
Supreme Allied Commander, South-East Asia

R6 SMURTHWAITE, David ed
THE FORGOTTEN WAR: The British Army in the Far East
1941–1945
National Army Museum 1992 207pp illustrated maps

Section S

Verses, Essays and Letters

S1 ALLEN, Louis
JAPAN: THE RECONCILIATION – OLD SOLDIERS NEVER DIE
A lecture presented to the Japan Society 26.4.90

S2 BEAUMONT, Stuart
FLASH POINTS: VERSES OF NOSTALGIA
194 Squadron Association 1994 31pp SC

S3 BIRCHALL, Stanley
POEMS
Unpublished 14pp
Author served in 1st Bn Royal Welch Fusiliers

S4 BRANSON, Clive
BRITISH SOLDIER IN INDIA: the letters of Clive Branson
Communist Party 1944 119pp illustrated SC
The author was a Troop Sgt Royal Armoured Corps when
killed in action February 25, 1944 at Ngakyedauk, Arakan.

S5 CALVER, D H
PADRE, PASTOR AND POET: Revd Kenneth W Parkhurst MBE
HCF 1907–1987: an account of his life and ministry together
with a selection of his poetry and prose
Privately printed 1988 78pp illustrated SC

S6 DAVEY, Mary
BACK TO BURMA FOR THE LOVE OF JOHN
Rathgar Press 1995 158pp illustrated SC
A quest for Uncle John and a pilgrimage to Thanbyuzat war
cemetery in lower Burma

S7 DONE, John
POEMS
6pp typescript

S8 GRAHAM, W Gordon
RETURN TO A BATTLEFIELD
Privately published 1994 6pp
Kohima: parallel English/Japanese text

S9 JAPAN DIGEST
INTERVIEW WITH LOUIS ALLEN: From Interrogator to
Interpreter

S10 LEWIS, Alun
IN THE GREEN TREE
Allen & Unwin 1948 141pp
Selection of letters and short stories

S11 LEWIS, Alun
LETTERS TO MY WIFE 1989 425pp edited by Gwen Lewis
COLLECTED STORIES 1990 367pp
COLLECTED POEMS 1994 206pp edited by Cary Archard
Seren (Poetry Wales Press)
Lewis served in the South Wales Borders, 36 Division and
died from an accidental gunshot wound at Bawli Bazaar,
Arakan, March 5, 1944

S12 LLEWELLYN-JONES, Dr Rosie
CHOWKIDAR 1977–1997
British Association for Cemeteries in South Asia 90pp
Illustrated SC
BACSA exists for the preservation of cemeteries and
memorials

S13 McEVOY, Patrick
BALLADS OF A BLACK CAT
Orrell Publications 1997 104pp illustrated map
Verse and prose: the Black Cat was divisional sign of 17th
Indian Division

S14 MOYNIHAN, Martin
BURMA
Private paper 1998 17pp typescript
Notes and random thoughts

S15 MOYNIHAN, Martin
SOUTH OF FORT HERTZ: a tale in rhyme
Mitre Press 1956 164pp

S16 NUNNELEY, John ed
TALES FROM THE BURMA CAMPAIGN 1942–1945
Burma Campaign Fellowship Group 1998 183pp
Sixty-one contributions by members of BCFG

S17 ROSS, Kathleen
STARS OF BURMA
Privately published poetry unpaged illustrated SC

S18 SLIM, William, Field Marshal the Viscount
COURAGE, AND OTHER BROADCASTS
Cassell 1957 186pp
Talks given in England, the US and Australia 1947–1957

S19 SLIM, William, Field Marshal the Viscount
CAMPAIGN OF THE FOURTEENTH ARMY 1943–1944
Printed by 476 Indian Printing Section 14pp Maps
Pamphlet with photographs

S20 STEVENSON, James
TWO POEMS

S21 THWAITES, Hugh S
WAR MEMOIRS OF AN AMATEUR
MA Associates 1997 76pp illustrated SC

S22 WATT, Matt
KOHIMA
Unpublished poem Ms

Section T

The War at Sea

Although the number of titles dealing with purely naval forces is small, there are references to the navy in the accounts of the Arakan Campaign and also the landing at Rangoon in 1945 in other sections.

T1   *HISTORY OF THE SECOND WORLD WAR
UK Military Series The War at Sea by S W Roskill 1954
Vol 1 The Defensive 664pp illustrated maps
Vol 2 The Period of balance 523pp illustrated maps
Vol 3 The Offensive 502pp illustrated maps

T2   *MINISTRY OF DEFENCE
Navy Historical Branch The War with Japan
HMSO 1955 6 volumes
Vol IV The South-East Asia operations ... 304pp illustrated
(separate folder of maps, Vols IV and V are bound together)
The results of the Naval Staff study

T3   BROWN, David ed
THE BRITISH PACIFIC AND EAST INDIES FLEETS 50TH
ANNIVERSARY 'THE FORGOTTEN FLEETS'
Liverpool: Brodie Publishing Ltd 118pp illustrated maps SC

T4   ELDRIDGE, A W C
JUST OUT OF SIGHT
Minerva Press 1998 322pp illustrated SC
A submariner and 'charioteer' on offensive underwater vehicles

T5   GOULDEN, O A
FROM TROMBAY TO CHANGI'S A HELLUVA WAY: the story of the Arakan Coastal Forces
Arakan Coastal Forces Reunion Committee 1987 229pp and appendices illustrated maps SC

T6 GOULDEN, O A
THE 13TH & 14TH FAIRMILE FLOTILLAS IN BURMA
Chameleon Press 1989 213pp illustrated
The operations of the Arakan Coastal Forces

T7 HASTINGS, D J
BOMBAY BUCCANEERS: memories and reminiscences of
the Royal Indian Navy
BACSA 1986 267pp illustrated

T8 POWER, Admiral Sir Arthur
DESPATCH: Naval Operations in the Ramree Island area
January19 to January 22, 1945 4pp map
(Supplement to *The London Gazette* April 23, 1948
no 38269)

T9 SPURR, Russell
LET THE TIGER TURN TAIL: SPURR'S WAR
Mainstream Publishing 1992 203pp illustrated
Adventures with Royal Indian Navy

T10 WRIGHT, Bruce S
THE FROGMEN OF BURMA: the story of the Sea
Reconnaissance Unit
Kimber 1970 170pp illustrated maps
A Royal Marine unit in Arakan at the Irrawaddy crossing

Section U

The War in the Air

U1   *ACSEA, Air Staff HQ
      AIR TRANSPORT OPERATIONS ON THE BURMA FRONT 1944

U2   AIR MINISTRY
      WINGS OF THE PHOENIX: the official story of the air war in
      Burma
      HMSO 1949 143pp illustrated maps

U3   *AYLING, Bob
      OLD LEATHERFACE OF THE FLYING TIGERS: the story of
      General Chennault
      Bobbs-Merrill 1945

U4   BATES, A S
      THE FLYING CARPET SALESMAN
      Privately published 1998 45pp illustrated maps SC
      Biography of J A G Mason 99 and 194 Squadron RAF

U5   *BEAUCHAMP, Gerry
      MOHAWKS OVER BURMA
      Shilton 1985 311pp illustrated

U6   BOWYER, Chaz
      BEAUFIGHTER AT WAR
      Ian Allan 1976 160pp illustrated
      One chapter on Burma

U7   BROWN, Atholl Sutherland
      SILENTLY INTO THE MIDST OF THINGS: 177 Squadron RAF in
      Burma – history and personal narratives
      Book Guild 1997 258pp illustrated
      Beaufighter interdiction of Japanese transport

U8   BURTON, F H
      MISSION TO BURMA: the story of 177 Squadron
      Blackburns of Bolton 1991 125pp illustrated map SC

U9 *CAIDIN, Martin
ZERO FIGHTER
Macdonald, 1970 160pp illustrated map

U10 CHINNERY, Philip D
ANY TIME, ANY PLACE: fifty years of the USAF Air
Commando and Special Operations Forces 1944–1994
Airlife 1994 303pp illustrated maps
Operations with the Chindits (Chapter 2)

U11 *CHENNAULT, Anna
CHENNAULT AND THE FLYING TIGERS
USA: Erikson

U12 *CHENNAULT, Claire Lee
WAY OF A FIGHTER
USA: Thorvardson 1991

U13 *CHENNAULT, Claire Lee
FLYING TIGER
Putnam

U14 COLLIS, Geoffrey R
THE EAGLE SOARS
Pentland Press 1998 116pp SC
273 (Spitfire) Squadron RAF in Arakan

U15 *COLLIS, Geoffrey R
THE TATTERED EAGLE
Pentland 1994

U16 COTTON, M C
HURRICANES OVER BURMA including The Memoirs of
Wing Commander 'Bunny' Stone, DFC
Grub Street 1995 357pp illustrated maps

U17 COURT, P R
THE FLYING 'TAXIS': 194 Squadron 'C' flight casualty
evacuation unit
Privately published 1998 92pp illustrated SC

U18 COYLE, F R ed
'CANUCKS UNLIMITED': 436 Squadron history
Canada n.d. 93pp illustrated
RCAF Dakota Squadron

U19 *DUNLOP, Richard
BURMA AIR VICTORY DECEMBER 1943 – JUNE 1945 (Eastern
Air Command)

U20 *ETHELL, J and DOWNIE
FLYING THE HUMP IN ORIGINAL WORLD WAR II COLOR
Motorbooks International 1995

U21 FORD, Daniel
FLYING TIGERS: Claire Chennault and the American
Volunteer Group
Smithsonian Institution Press 1991 463pp map SC

U22 *FRANKS, Norman
FIRST IN THE INDIAN SKIES
Life Publications 1991

U23 FRANKS, Norman L R
HURRICANES OVER THE ARAKAN
Patrick Stephens 1989 237pp illustrated maps

U24 FRANKS, Norman L R
THE AIR BATTLE OF IMPHAL
Kimber 1985 223pp illustrated map

U25 FRANKS, Norman L R
SPITFIRES OVER THE ARAKAN
Kimber 1988 231pp illustrated maps

U26 FRANKS, Norman and RICHEY
FIGHTER PILOT'S SUMMER
Grub Street 1993 248pp illustrated

U27 GOLDNEY, Frank Hammond
WAR DIARIES AND MEMOIRS
Australia: Hyde Park Press 155pp illustrated SC
117 Squadron RAF (Dakotas) from 1944

U28 GWYNNE-TIMOTHY, John R W
BURMA LIBERATORS: RCAF IN SEAC
Canada: Next Level Press 1991 2 volumes 1155pp
illustrated SC

U29 HEIFERMAN, Ron
FLYING TIGERS: CHENNAULT IN CHINA
Ballantine 1971 160pp illustrated SC

U30 HEMINGWAY, Kenneth
WINGS OVER BURMA
Quality press 1944 190pp illustrated
17 (Fighter) Squadron

U31 HENDERSON, Lt Col W
CHINA BURMA INDIA
Waco, Texas, US: Texian Press 149pp
US Air Force bombing missions

U32 *HOTZ, R B
WITH GENERAL CHENNAULT: the story of the Flying Tigers
USA: Zenger 1980

U33 HUDSON, Lionel
THE RATS OF RANGOON: the inside story of the 'fiasco' that
took place at the end of the war in Burma
Leo Cooper 1987 230pp
Written by Air Force Officer

U34 HUMP PILOTS ASSOCIATION
CHINA, BURMA, INDIA
US: Turner Publishing Company 392pp illustrated
Collection of newsletters

U35 INNES, David J
BEAUFIGHTERS OVER BURMA
Blandford Press 1985 128pp illustrated maps
27 Squadron RAF

U36 JACOBS, Vivian K
THE WOODPECKER STORY, as told by members of No 136
(Fighter) Squadron RAF 'The Woodpeckers'
Pentland press 1994 261pp illustrated map

U37 JONES, Laurie
A PILOT'S STORY OF FLYING IN WAR AND PEACE
Australia: privately printed 1996 259pp illustrated map
Part 1 covers air operations in Bay of Bengal

U38 KOENIG, William J
OVER THE HUMP: AIRLIFT TO CHINA
Pan/Ballantine 1972 160pp illustrated SC

U39 LAL, Pratap Chandra
MY YEARS WITH THE IAF
New Delhi: Lancer International 1986 396pp
Chapter 3 covers his service with the India Air Force during
the Burma Campaign

U40 LAW W C ed
CHINTHE – BURMA/INDIA 1944–1945
Canada n.d. 166pp illustrated
435 RCAF Squadron (Dakota)

U41 *LOSONSKY, F S and T M
FLYING TIGER: A CREW CHIEF'S STORY. The war diary of an
AVG crew chief
Schiffer 1996

U42 MASLEN-JONES, E W
FIRE BY ORDER: recollections of service with 656 Air
Observation Post Squadron in Burma
Leo Cooper 1997 207pp illustrated maps

U43 MASON, Peter D
NICOLSON, V C
Ashford: Geerings 1991 164pp illustrated
Nicolson served in 27 Squadron RAF in Burma

U44 MORRIS, Dickson G
BEYOND THE IRRAWADDY AND THE SALWEEN: RAF special
duty missions in the South-East Asia theatre of war
1944–1945
Australia: Mostly Unsung 1996 183pp illustrated SC

U45 MOXON, Oliver
BITTER MONSOON: the memoirs of a fighter pilot
Robert Hale 1955 192pp illustrated map
5 (Fighter Squadron) RAF

U46 NALTY, Bernard C
TIGERS OVER ASIA
New York: Elsevier-Dutton 1978 182pp illustrated
The American Volunteer Group 'The Flying Tigers'

U47 O'BRIEN, Terence
CHASING AFTER DANGER: a combat pilot's war over Europe
and the Far East 1939–1942
Collins 1990 264 pp

U48 OPERATION THURSDAY
FILE OF PHOTOCOPIES signals relating to Allied landings in
North East Burma 48pp

U49 O'REGAN, Harley
NOTES on life on an Air Transport and Supply Squadron
during the Burma Campaign of World War II
Sydney: privately published n.d. 120pp

U50 *PAGE, Robert C and AITKEN
AIR COMMAND DOC
Ackerman 1945

U51 PARHAM, H J and BELFIELD
UNARMED INTO BATTLE: the story of the Air Observation
Post
Picton, for the Army Air Corps 2nd ed 1986 183pp
illustrated maps

U52 *PARK, Air Chief Marshal Sir Keith
DESPATCH: Air operations in South-East Asia from June 1,
1944 to the re-occupation of Rangoon May 2, 1945
(Supplement to *The London Gazette* April 6, 1951
no 39196)

U53 *PARRY, J F
Burma Volunteer Air Force 1940–1942
Privately published

U54 *PEIRSE, Air Vice Marshal Sir Richard
Despatch: Air operations in South-East Asia November 16,
1943 to May 31, 1944 27pp map
(Supplement to *The London Gazette* March 13, 1951 no
39173)

U55 *PISTOLE, Larry
The Pictorial history of the Flying tigers
Moss 1981

U56 PROBERT, Henry
The Forgotten Air Force: the Royal Air Force in the war
against Japan 1941–1945
Brassey's 1995 381pp illustrated maps

U57 *RAWLINSON, Peter
Calamity Jane: by Spitfire to India
The author

U58 ROSHOLT, Malcolm
Days of the Ching Pao: a photographic record of the
Flying Tigers – 14th Air Force in China in World War II
Appleton, Wisconsin: Rosholt House II 4th ed 1986 192pp
illustrated

U59 ROYAL AIR FORCE HISTORICAL SOCIETY
The RAF and the Far East War 1941–1945:
a symposium ...
RAF Historical Society 1995 129pp illustrated maps
Various contributors on whom there are biographical notes

U60 RUSSELL, W W
Forgotten skies: the story of the Air Forces in India and
Burma
Hutchinson 1945 128pp illustrated maps

U61 *RUSSELL, Wilfred W
The Friendly firm: a history of 194 Squadron RAF
194 Squadron Wing Association 1972

U62 *SAMSON, J
CHENNAULT
Doubleday 1987

U63 SANSOME, R S
THE BAMBOO WORKSHOP: the history of the RAF repair
and salvage units India/Burma 1941–1946
Merlin Books 1995 213pp illustrated SC

U64 SCOTT, Robert Lee
FLYING TIGER: CHENNAULT OF CHINA
New York: Berkley Publishing 1960 220pp SC

U65 SHORES, Christopher and others
BLOODY SHAMBLES Vol 2 The defence of Sumatra to the
Fall of Burma
Grub Street 1993 494pp illustrated map
Comprehensive account of air operations

U66 SMITH, Peter
VENGEANCE
Airlife 1986
The Vultee Vengeance was a single-engined dive bomber
used by two squadrons of the Indian Air Force in Burma.

U67 SPENCER, Otha C
FLYING THE HUMP: memories of an air war
Texas: A & M University 1992 illustrated maps

U68 STEVENSON, Air Vice Marshal D F
DESPATCH: Air operations in Burma and the Bay of Bengal
January 1 to May 22, 1942 21pp
(Supplement to *The London Gazette* March 5, 1958 no
38229)

U69 STONES, Donald
OPERATION 'BOGRAT' FROM FRANCE TO BURMA
Spellmount Ltd 1990 128pp illustrated
67 (Fighter) Squadron

U70 SUTCLIFFE, D H
AIRBORNE OVER BURMA
Published by the author 1988
62 Squadron with Dakotas

U71 SUTTON, Barry
JUNGLE PILOT
Macmillan 1946 134pp

U72 *SZUSCIKIEWICZ, P
FLYING TIGERS
Bison Books 1990 80pp illustrated

U73 *TAYLOR, Joe G
AIR SUPPLY IN THE BURMA CAMPAIGN
USAF History Division, Air University 1957

U74 THOMAS, J Helsdon
WINGS OVER BURMA
New Horizon 1984
Merlon 1991 91pp illustrated maps SC
67 Fighter Squadron 1942–1944

U75 *UNITED STATES ARMY AIR FORCE
BURMA OPERATIONS RECORD 1952 (revised 1957)

U76 VAN WAGNER, R D
1ST AIR COMMAND GROUP AIR COMMAND AND
STAFF COLLEGE
Air University Maxwell Air Force Base, Alabama
Student report 1986 96pp illustrated map m/s

U77 WHARTON, Ray
PHOTOGRAPHS OF AIRCRAFT IN AIR HQ (INDIA)
COMMUNICATIONS SQUADRON

U78 WHELAN, Russell
THE FLYING TIGERS: the story of the American
Volunteer Group
New York: Viking 1942 224pp illustrated map

U79 WILLIAMS, Douglas
194 SQUADRON RAF 'THE FRIENDLY FIRM'
Merlin Books 1987 80pp illustrated SC

U80 WILLIAMS, Douglas
194 SQUADRON RAF
Various unpublished typescripts including an appreciation
of General Wingate 2pp; RAF Dakota Training Unit SEAC
2pp; a brief history of 194 Squadron by Arthur Pearcy 11pp;
etc

Section V

Fiction

V1 ALDISS, Brian W
A SOLDIER ERECT, OR FURTHER ADVENTURES OF
THE HAND-REARED BOY
Corgi Books 1974 222pp SC

V2 ALEXANDER, K
THE FORGOTTEN ARMY
Regular Publications 1996 160pp SC

V3 ANDREWS, Laurie W
OF LESSER RENOWN
Cassell 1958 264pp

V4 ANDREWS, Laurie W
THE PATROL
Corgi 1972 172pp

V5 *ANDREWS, Laurie W
TATTERED BATTALION
Cassell 1957 223pp

V6 ANDREWS, Laurie W
DEATH MARCH
Corgi 1960 286pp SC

V7 *BAILLIE, Peter
CHINDWIN MONSOON
Brown Watson 1958 155pp SC

V8 BARDEN, Stanley
THE GOLDEN ROCK OF KYAIK-TIYO
United Writers 1997 262 pp
Book Two of the Burma Ruby Series

V9 BATES, H E
THE PURPLE PLAIN
Michael Joseph 1947 224pp

V10 BATES, H E
THE JACARANDA TREE
Michael Joseph 1949 223pp

V11 BAXTER, Walter
LOOK DOWN IN MERCY
Heinemann 1951 288pp

V12 BAXTER, Walter
THE IMAGE AND THE SEARCH
Heinemann 1953 332pp

V13 BELL, Gerard
SIDESHOW
Corgi Books 251 pp SC

V14 *BLACK, Dorothy
FANTASTIC JOURNEY
Cassell 1944 191pp

V15 BLANKENSHIP, William D
TIGER TEN
New York: Putnam 252 pp

V16 *BRADDON, Russell
END OF A HATE
Cassell 1958 201pp
Incorporating Song of war: a short story

V17 BRADDON, Russell
SONG OF WAR
M/s

V18 *BRELIS, Dean
THE MISSION
Constable 1959 180pp

V19 *BRENDON, George
THE CHARM OF MAMBAS
Heinemann 1959 279pp

V20 *BROOKES, April
FOLLOW YOUR STAR
Ward Lock 1956 190pp

V21 BUCK, Pearl S
THE PROMISE
Moyer Bell, Wakefield, Rhode Island, USA reprinted 1997
248pp
Methuen 1944

V22 BUTTERWORTH, Sidney
THREE RIVERS TO GLORY
Hutchinson 1956 224pp

V23 *CAREW, Tim
MAN FOR MAN
Constable 1955 230pp

V24 CHAMALES, Tom T
NEVER SO FEW
New York: Scribners 1957 499pp

V25 CHANG, C T
BURMA ROAD
Singapore: Malaysia Publications Ltd 1964 198pp

V26 CLIFFORD, Francis
A BATTLE IS FOUGHT TO BE WON
Pan 1960 125pp SC

V27 CLIFFORD, Francis
HONOUR THE SHRINE
Transworld 1960 19pp SC

V28 CLIFFORD, J F
KAMIKAHSE (DIVINE TEMPEST)
Private paper n.d. 23pp typescript
Fiction based on service in Burma 1944–1945 JFC

V29 CONWAY, P
THE PALINDROME
Dakers 1951 222pp

v30 *COOPER, Brian
Van langeren girl
Heinemann 1960 222pp

v31 CROOK, William
Four days
Eyre Methuen 1979 172pp

v32 CRUMPLER, Gus H
Under the Burmese Pagoda
Point Lookout, Missouri: The School of the Ozarks Press
1975 148pp

v33 CRUTTWELL, Patrick
A Kind of fighting
J M Dent 1959 272pp

v34 *DONALDSON, D H
The Lone Chindit
Hale 1967 190pp

v35 *ELDER, Raiheart
After my own fashion
Longmans Green 1949 239pp

v36 EYRE, Donald C
Foxes have holes
Hale 1948 287pp

v37 FENN, Charles
The Golden rule of General Wong
Arthur Barker 1960 150pp

v38 FINLAY, Bernard
Bamboo Hell
Peter Haddock 1980 158pp sc

v39 FORSTER, Roy
The Flute of Asoka
Eyre & Spottiswoode 1955 272pp

V40 FORSYTH, R A
SQUADRON WILL MOVE
Macmillan 1947 311pp

V41 FRIEND, John
THE LONG TREK
Muller 1957 187pp

V42 *GILLESPIE, Leslie
THE MAN FROM MADURA
Boardman 1952 255pp

V43 GORDON, John W
WINGS FROM BURMA TO THE HIMALAYAS
Memphis: Global Press 1987 265pp

V44 *GRIFFIN, Sercombe
BURMA ROAD CALLING!
Harrap 1943 206pp

V45 HANLEY, Gerald
SEE YOU IN YASUKUNI
Collins 1969 224pp

V46 HORSLEY, D
LIVING DEAD
Brown Watson 1959 157pp SC

V47 JACKSON, I K
STRIKING FORCE
Trojan [1965?] no pagination SC

V48 *JOHNS, W E
BIGGLES AND THE LOST SOVEREIGNS
Brockhampton Press 1964 164pp Junior fiction

V49 JOHNSTON, G H
DEATH TAKES SMALL BITES
Gollancz 1948 199pp

V50 JOHNSTON, Jack
PATROL OF THE DEAD
Arthur Barker 1955 239pp

v51 LEASOR, James
NOTHING TO REPORT
Viking 1955 254pp sc

v52 *MADDOCK, Reginald B
ONE MORE RIVER
Nelson 1963 156pp illustrated

v53 MANNIN, Ethel
THE LIVING LOTUS
New York: Putnam 1956 255pp

v54 MARKS, J M
AYO GURKHA!
OUP 1971 189pp illustrated map
Junior Fiction

v55 MASON, Richard
THE WIND CANNOT READ
Hodder & Stoughton 1946 296pp

v56 MILLER, Lee O
ASSIGNMENT: BURMA
New York: Belmont Tower Books 176pp sc

v57 MOISEIWITSCH, Maurice
YESTERDAY'S ENEMY
Transworld 158pp sc

v58 MOXON, Oliver
AFTER THE MONSOON
Robert Hale 1958 160pp

v59 MOXON, Oliver
THE LAST MONSOON
Elmfield Press 1957 174pp

v60 *MUCHA, Jiri
SCORCHED CROP
Hogarth Press 1949 271pp

v61 NATHANSON, E M
THE DIRTY DISTANT WAR
New York: Viking 1987 484pp

v62 PARTINGTON, Norman
THE GATES OF THE KYSAN
Harrap 1971 270pp

v63 *PHILLIPS, J A
PAGODA
Bodley Head 1953 155pp

v64 *PUGH, Marshall
THE CHANCER
Hutchinson 1959 199pp

v65 RENNIE, D J
PENETRATION FORCE
John Spencer 1959 157pp SC

v66 RICHARDS, C J
WIND OVER FOWLMERE AND OTHER STORIES
Winchester: Warren & Sons 1953 217pp

v67 *ROLAND, Paul K
'BANZAI'
John Spencer 1959 159pp SC

v68 * ROSS, Kenneth
RICKY & CO AIR COMMANDOS
Cambridge University Press 1947 162pp
Junior Fiction

v69 *RUTHIN, Margaret
JUNGLE NURSE
Dobson 1960 190pp Junior fiction

v70 SAUL, John Ralston
THE NEXT BEST THING
Grafton Books 1986 241pp

V71 *SCOTT, J M
WHERE THE RIVER BENDS
Heinemann 1962 249pp

V72 SCOTT, Paul
JOHNNY SAHIB
Granada 1979 208pp SC

V73 SCOTT, Paul
THE MARK OF THE WARRIOR
Granada 1979 188pp SC

V74 SHUTE, Nevil
THE CHEQUER BOARD
Heinemann 1947 278pp

V75 SIBLEY, John
YOU'LL WALK TO MANDALAY
Cape 1960 253pp

V76 STANFORD, J K
LAST CHUKKER
Faber & Faber 1941 76pp illustrated

V77 STANFORD, J K
REVERIE OF QU-HAI AND OTHER STORIES
Blackwood 1951 332pp

V78 STERN, D
FRANCIS
Hammond 150 255pp

V79 *STUART, Vivian
LIFE IS DESTINY
Robert Hale 1958 192pp

V80 TARMEY, Martin
WHEN YOU GO HOME: the bloody battle of Kohima Ridge
Corgi 1975 320pp SC

v81 TAYLOR, Thomas
      BORN OF WAR
      McGraw-Hill 1988 450pp
      A novel based on Wingate

v82 *TURNBULL, Patrick
      LIKE AN ABOMINABLE BRANCH
      Hurst & Blackett 1947 188pp

v83 TURNBULL, Patrick
      THE LAST OF MEN
      Hutchinson 1960 223pp

v84 TURNBULL, Patrick
      ONE BULLET FOR THE GENERAL
      Collins 1969 224pp

v85 *WAKEFORD, L H and JARMEY
      BROWN MEN'S JUNGLE
      E J Arnold 1951 128pp illustrated

v86 *WALLACE, J H
      A WALK IN THE FOREST
      Brown Watson 159pp SC

Section W
Japanese books in English

Only books translated or written originally in English are included in this section. There will be a separate catalogue at a later date of books in Japanese.

W1 AIDI, Yugi
PRISONER OF THE BRITISH
Cresset Press 1966 202pp

W2 BARKER, A J
JAPANESE ARMY HANDBOOK 1939–1945
Ian Allan 1979 128pp illustrated

W3 HAYASHI, Saburo with COOX
KOGUN: THE JAPANESE ARMY IN THE PACIFIC WAR
USA: Marine Corps Ass 1959 245pp illustrated maps SC

W4 HIRAKUBO, Masao and others
THE JAPANESE SOLDIER
Papers given at seminar organized by the Burma Campaign
Fellowship Group 1996 22pp

W5 *ISOBE, Tokuo
IRRAWADDY SHORE AND THE MEIKTILA OPERATION
Japan 1998

W6 NISHIJI, Yasumasa
'THOSE FORSAKEN BY GOD': the retreat from Imphal
The author 14pp SC

W7 TAKEYAMA, Michio
HARP OF BURMA
Rutland Vermont: CE Tuttle 1966 132pp SC

W8 TAMAYAMA, Kazuo
JAPANESE SOLDIERS OF THE BURMA CAMPAIGN
Book One January – March 1942
The author 42pp illustrated map

W9   *TATSURO, Izumiya
THE MINAMI ORGAN
U Soe Myint 1981

W10 US Department of the Army Office of the Chief of
Military History
BURMA OPERATIONS RECORD:
28th Army Ops in Akyab area 1958 210 pp maps SC
15th Army Ops in Imphal area and withdrawal to North
Burma 1957 189pp maps SC
Prepared by Japanese staff officers and commanders

W11 US War Department: Military Intelligence Service
SOLDIER'S GUIDE TO THE JAPANESE ARMY
Washington DC 1944 182pp illustrated SC

W12 WADA, Manabu
DRIFTING DOWN THE CHINDWIN
The author 27pp SC

Addenda